PROMOTING MENTAL HEALTH
OF OLDER PEOPLE
THROUGH
GROUP METHODS

———

A Practical Guide

PROMOTING MENTAL HEALTH
OF OLDER PEOPLE
THROUGH
GROUP METHODS

A Practical Guide

WILMA H. KLEIN, EDA J. LE SHAN,
and SYLVAN S. FURMAN

Published for
THE MANHATTAN SOCIETY FOR MENTAL HEALTH, INC.
by the
MENTAL HEALTH MATERIALS CENTER, INC.
104 East 25th Street, New York, N. Y. 10010

THE DEMONSTRATION PROJECT WHICH LED TO THE WRITING OF THIS BOOK WAS SUPPORTED BY A GRANT FROM THE AARON E. NORMAN FUND AND CONTRIBUTIONS FROM THE SUPPORTERS OF THE MANHATTAN SOCIETY FOR MENTAL HEALTH.

GRATEFUL ACKNOWLEDGEMENT IS HEREBY MADE TO ALL THOSE WHOSE CONCERN FOR THE WELL-BEING OF OUR AGED CITIZENS MADE THIS WORK POSSIBLE.

Contents

5

DEDICATED TO
THE MEMBERS OF THE GROUPS
WHO SHARED WITH US
THEIR THOUGHTS AS
OLDER PEOPLE.

Preface

ALVIN I. GOLDFARB, M.D.
Consultant on Services for the Aged
New York State Department of Mental Hygiene

Attending Associate Psychiatrist and
Chief of Geriatric Psychiatry
Mount Sinai Hospital, New York

Taking age 65 as the time when people become old, older persons now comprise about 11 per cent of our population as compared to 3 per cent some 60 years ago. Among this population, which numbers almost 20,000,000 persons, are a very large number of depressed, puzzled and bewildered men and women.

It is inconceivable that there will be at any time enough psychiatrists to handle all the psychiatric problems this population will pose. It is imperative that society take very seriously the now well-known statements of Adolph Meyer that it is the doctor's job to help the community dispense with its need for the physician.

The authors of this book have obviously thought about this problem and are making attempts to assist the community toward reorganizing itself in such a way as to ease the suffering in selected groups of its aged members, and to decrease the disturbances that their distress may cause their families and society. In my opinion, the writers have chosen what might be called a group psychotherapeutic approach and in this book they describe the selection of their groups and the leaders, the problems that are discussed, and what they believe to be useful attitudes on the part of the leader so that the individual members may derive benefit in the sense of increased comfort and useful information for better life adjustment.

Younger persons in group psychotherapy may be said to go through a process in which they make, break, remake, test, use, discard, decide upon and consolidate relationships with others in the group and in this process they may acquire what we call insight—they learn a lot about themselves and about other persons. When this insight is not only verbal or intellectual but is coordinated with feeling or emotion so that it has meaning for the person and contributes to improved relationships, then we feel signally successful. However, older persons do not seem to go through this process in their groups, no matter what the intent or skill of the leader or psychotherapist.

What shines through the statements that follow is that older persons bring practical problems to the leader, that they focus their attention upon him, and that they benefit from the opportunity to bring things to him and from his attitude toward them. Their fellow group members are, in a way, incidental, but they may be necessary and the group setting may be needed if they are to form an attachment to anyone— in this case the group leader—at all. Even where the group is unnecessary for the individual aged person, it may not be obstructive and may not interfere with the benefit he may derive from the development of a relationship with the leader. Because it favors the development of a relationship which the older person may otherwise be disinclined to accept or may be unable to find, the group may prove to be a practical —as well as a less expensive—way of providing what many aged persons need if they are to learn, relearn or release their capacities for adjustment to a community which tends to pose them difficult problems as their ability decreases.

I hope that this book's attempt to outline the characteristics of some of our aged population, some methods of welding persons with problems into groups, and some ways of assisting them to establish a relationship with a group leader will further our society's efforts to organize itself so as to profit from, but lean less upon, the specialist psychiatrist.

Introduction

It has long ago ceased to be news that due to a greater average life span, our culture's emphasis on youth, trends toward earlier retirement, and other reasons, there are many problems about the aging in our society. These range from the urgent need for comprehensive medical care programs that older people can afford, to such problems as what to do with one's leisure time and how to make it possible for the aged to live out their lives constructively and with a continuing sense of purpose and dignity.

Many American communities have responded to these needs by establishing "senior citizen" centers or by adapting or expanding the work of community centers, churches and other organizations to serve the aging. These centers have programs that vary from those affording aged persons the simple opportunity to get together, to more elaborate programs aimed at supplying both group and individual services to fulfill a wide range of needs. This work also varies greatly in scope, quality and significance for the people it seeks to serve. While almost all of it is of some value—much of it valuable indeed—it has seemed to us, among others, that it is too often patterned on prior experience in working with younger generations. There has been a tendency to overlook the fact that the persons for whom such programs are devised have usually been self-sustaining, self-directing citizens for many years; they have raised families, worked for a living, carried out their responsibilities as independent citizens, and coped more or less adequately with the problems of life.

While infirmities and illnesses tend to increase or become more of a problem in the later years, the fact of being aged is not in itself an illness. With others, we hold that being old is one stage of living, like childhood, adolescence and adulthood; the fact that this stage is accompanied by failing powers is a serious complication but is no excuse for disregarding or dismissing the values of maturity, perspective and often widsom that can come with old age.

Yet many of the well-meant programs that have been organized for the aging and the aged have more or less unwittingly proceeded from the viewpoint that older persons cannot plan for themselves or continue to develop satisfying friendships or derive social and emotional satisfactions from daily living. Accordingly, many of the programs for the aging have tended to infantilize older people through the very nature of the activities planned for them, rather than to involve them in the planning itself, or to assist them in using their leisure time to explore the burning issues of living, to continue their changing social and family relationships, and to cope independently with the practical concerns that develop after retirement.

This book has been written to help those who work with the aged in community settings to avoid these pitfalls. It is intended to help equip these workers with skills and techniques that can enrich existing programs, at little or no extra cost, by aiding their aged members to utilize their assets of personality, leisure time and continuing relationships in constructive ways. We believe that the absence of such opportunities can be harmful to the mental health of the aging, which is already vulnerable through the assaults of physical illness and deterioration. Having such opportunities will not cure physical ailments, but it can well help to relieve much of the stress of loneliness and the sense of futility in many older people.

It was in this spirit that we undertook the formal experiment that is reported more fully in the appendix of this book. It was not only our conviction but that of the participants that the project was a successful one. There were many evidences not only of the satisfactions gained by the aging persons who made up our discussion groups, but also of positive effects on other work done in the host programs.

What we did is easily described. With the cooperation of established centers which had been serving the aged in various ways, we held weekly discussions with small groups of the members. These discussions dealt with things they themselves wanted to talk about—

their present, past and future concerns. Some of the subject matter was of a practical nature, such as how to improve their living conditions, the best arrangements to make for health care, or the problems of living on fixed, limited incomes. Other subjects were more general —relationships with grown children and with grandchildren, attitudes of society toward the aging, the pace and flavor of present-day and earlier modes of living. Various techniques were used in leading these discussions and the leader assumed a variety of roles within the group. But one thing never varied, and that was her basic respect for the capacities of the members, their desire to conduct and manage their own affairs as fully as possible within their means and capacities; another, her avoidance of patronizing or "directing" attitudes. This approach was clearly appreciated by the vast majority of those who participated, as was demonstrated by the variety and richness of their response.

While professional training certainly is desirable, it is not essential that this kind of work be done by leaders who are fully trained in group leadership methods. (The question is almost an academic one, so great is the shortage of trained workers who are assigned to this work.) This book, which is among other things a "how to do it" manual, aims to help the average worker in such centers use his own personality and intelligence in providing this type of service. Knowing the financial limitations and other burdens involved in maintaining and operating centers and other programs for the aged, we would be less than realistic to advocate elaborate approaches to discussion group programs. We think that this is in any case unnecessary. The abilities, energy, good sense and "understanding heart" of the vast majority of workers already in the field, if properly used, can serve to build more satisfying and constructive programs for the ever-growing numbers of older persons living in the community.

Sylvan S. Furman
Executive Director
Manhattan Society for Mental Health

November 1, 1965

PROMOTING MENTAL HEALTH OF OLDER PEOPLE THROUGH GROUP METHODS

A Practical Guide

CHAPTER ONE

Mental Health Discussion Groups and How They Work

In a broad sense, a discussion is a conversation in which the goal is communication, shared experience. One can talk without conversing, converse without communicating, and communicate without analysis or criticism. . . . The function of a genuine discussion is to examine one's ideas, feelings, attitudes and opinions with a view toward modifying them, to incorporate another's idea or insight. Thus by sharing in the experience of another, communication takes place.

> —Bernard M. Shiffman, "Effecting Social Change through Social Group Work," National Conference on Social Welfare, Chicago, 1958.

Much of the new knowledge that has been developed as a result of twentieth century discoveries can be transmitted by traditional methods of learning and teaching. Vast and impressive progress has been made in our understanding of the physical world; yet the new information can usually be taught in ways that are not drastically different from those used before. This has not been true, however, in the field of mental health.

In a general sense, the development of modern mental health concepts began with the work of Freud and his followers. Through the genius of his explorations into the basic nature of man, new—indeed, revolutionary—insights were acquired into human behavior and social relationships.

As the fields of psychiatry and psychology developed, it became apparent that while their original hypotheses were developed out of investigations into pathology, psychological distress and illness, the findings had meaning not only for the improvement and refinement of healing procedures but also for the prevention of mental disorders. Just as the increased understanding of physical ailments, their causes and cures, had led to broad programs of public health education aimed at prevention and early intervention, increased understanding of mental illness led specialists to hope that public education in this area could lead to a reduction in the incidence of mental ills.

But how could the new material best be taught? Many have attempted to transmit the new concepts in the old way, through academic methods, on an intellectual level, not only to professionals—doctors, nurses, social workers, family life specialists, psychologists, psychiatrists—but also to the general public. It has been amply demonstrated, however, that students on all levels, including citizens-at-large, are unable to use this knowledge effectively unless it is genuinely incorporated into themselves, emotionally as well as intellectually. Charged with emotion, these new insights are subjective and call forth subjective personal responses. Mental health educators therefore found they could not concern themselves merely with disseminating information. They had to recognize the psychological impact of the new material and find new ways to transmit it, ways that would permit the facts to be integrated with the individual's outlook and reactions. As we shall see, one approach that has proved effective in achieving this kind of communication in a wide variety of situations is that of the mental health education discussion group.

Education, Social Work, Therapy

It may be worthwhile to stop for a moment at this point to consider a matter that may cause some confusion to laymen and is of major concern at times to professionals—the differences, and similarities, between mental health education, social group work, work in group dynamics, and group psychotherapy.

The area with which this book is concerned—mental health education—is given over primarily to the prevention of emotional illness and distress. The educator works with people who are healthy enough in their relationships with others to get along adequately in day-to-day, real-life situations. The same could be said of social group work, although recently more and more of this work has been done in institutions, or in specially organized situations serving the disturbed personality. In both approaches, however, the intent is to preserve and foster the social health already existing; to help the individual identify and use his strengths rather than to focus on his difficulties. Both approaches try to build the resources for health, to enrich and reinforce rather than to explore deeply and change radically. In this way education differs sharply from therapy, which concerns itself much more directly with pathology or illness.

As we have seen, the development of therapeutic techniques preceded the development of new educational methods and some few specialists have never looked beyond therapy. They consider direct, individual counseling and psychotherapy the only real way of aiding individuals facing mental health crises at any stage of life. Such services, however, are in short supply. Although they have become increasingly available to children and young adults, they are few and far between for older people. Furthermore, at the other extreme there are those who feel that individual, intensive psychotherapy is not desirable or possible with older persons and a few who feel that the elderly, set in their ways, are unable to use or even to achieve psychological insights for emotional reorientation.

Our experience has shown—and the remaining chapters of this book will, we trust, demonstrate—that educational methods are successful with those elderly persons who are not suffering serious impairments and who have normal ego strengths. For such individuals the information, guidance and new insights to be gained through the discussion group can be of major importance as they strive to meet the psychological challenges of aging. It is true that the aged are subject to degenerative, irreversible processes that can disable and handicap them. In large part it is these that account for the high rate of admissions of the elderly to mental hospitals. But stress, we are convinced, also plays a part in precipitating much mental illness—and a vast amount of general unhappiness—among the aged. For those still functioning adequately, then, the mental health education group, by helping its members meet their problems more effectively, appears an especially suitable technique for keeping stress at a minimum.

Development of Group Methods

What is the background of such groups? How have they proved their effectiveness? Well over half a century of experimentation with methods and procedures has gone into the development of group techniques to bring about meaningful learning in this area.

Because so much preventive mental health work has been related to family life and child development, it was natural that parent education should become the focus of most of the earliest and more intensive experimentation. Child study groups were already meeting in the late 1800's—usually groups of mothers trying to study and discuss the new information that was beginning to emerge. Parent education is the "grandfather of mental health education" in the sense that most of the basic goals and methods of the currently expanding field of mental health education derive from the experience and background gained through work with parents. Parent educators who work with groups have been wrestling for many years with such questions as:

—How can mental health concepts be presented in the most effective ways?

—What represents the most appropriate and effective kind of group leadership?

—What kinds of group experiences encourage personal growth?

—How do we find a balance between expert information on the one hand and the need for individual acceptance of such information through personal involvement on the other?

Social work out of its own approach, and also using concepts from psychiatry, psychology and education, has made its special contribution to mental health education through the group work methods. The 1930's saw the addition of social group work to the practice of social work.

Social group workers began with some of the same questions about leadership, individual growth and personal involvement that mental health educators had faced. They turned to existing social work practice, based upon a knowledge of individual behavior, in order to shape the fundamentals of social group work, which they saw as a medium for fostering social health, characterized by democratic behavior. The process from which this activity evolves takes place in the real-life laboratories of groups as people experience the intellectual stimulation of give-and-take, as they digest information, exchange ideas, compromise, arrive at decisions; as they discover the joy of experiencing real rapport with other people, making new friends; evaluating failures, bouncing back, learning from mistakes and from each other. Thus, working together in groups, trying to solve common concerns through earnest communication, people have a workshop in which to perfect the human skills required for democratic behavior and the development of democratic leaders.

Advantages of Groups

The process through which these reactions emerge is basically dependent upon group discussion through individual involvement. The art of the discussion leader, skillfully exercised, provides the framework in which the goals of education, growth and change can be achieved. The exchange that takes place among people working together in groups offers some the opportunity to feel competent and able about the things they know, to experience mastery when they have learned a new skill or new information, and to be stimulated to want to develop further their personality potentials.

These goals and observations concerning the methods of social group work may be fruitfully compared with aims set down by mental health educators with special interest in parent education. A conference of parent group leaders meeting several years ago under the auspices of the New York State Bureau of Child Development and Parent Education formulated the general goals of mental health education. The approach used in such work, they held, should provide experiences that enrich the lives of the group members and increase their sense of their own inner resources; it should help release spontaneous creativity and add to a person's capacity to relate warmly to others. The content offered should serve to strengthen and broaden perspective and understanding. Leadership should have flexibility, be able to communicate feelings, express warmth and concern, be able to universalize experience, respect differences, encourage growth through new explorations and—most important—respect the health within the group.

In somewhat similar fashion, the Child Study Association describes the parents' group as enabling its members to gain a feeling of mutuality, to pinpoint their concerns, to receive positive recognition of their desire to be effective parents, to see themselves mirrored in the acts and statements of others, to acquire sound self-knowledge and information, to discover or express the assumptions that underlie their behavior, to explore and consider the many ways of dealing with the perplexities of everyday living, and to find support and recognition of their right to be different.

In view of what has been said about social group work, it is easy to see how these goals would be mutually compatible and why the methods of each field would be useful to the other.

Social Group Work vs. Mental Health Education

There are some differences in emphasis, however, and perhaps the auspices under which most social group work activity is carried on—the social agency—provides the key to the differences. Whereas the content of most mental health education groups primarily concerns behavior and the discussion of some fact, theory or experience related to it, the content discussed in social group work programs may relate to a skill, an activity, social issues or intellectual pursuits, or to some aspect of human behavior. Any of these may serve as the channel through which members may be helped to deal with the challenges of everyday living. Social group work is therefore committed to help group members explore and consider alternatives, but beyond that, it actively tries to enable members to take some direct action when appropriate. As we move into mental health education with our elder citizens and golden age clubs and centers, we are likely to do so in cooperation with sponsoring social agencies which have the commitment to serve as vehicles for initiating this direct action. The work reported here gives examples of how this commitment can be practically applied when one combines the techniques, methods and philosophies of both social group work and mental health education.

Another difference (again related to sponsorship) is the stress which social group work puts upon developing indigenous leadership. It is important to examine, explore and understand, but in addition it is important to assume leadership responsibility for the improvement or elimination of individual or common concerns. If we are to encourage people to grow, to broaden their perspectives, to shape their own lives, and possibly to effect appropriate social change, then it would seem that social group work can greatly enhance these processes by helping people to step forward and take leadership responsibility for action. Because such action can increase people's sense of mastery, increase self-esteem and yield great ego satisfaction, mental health as well as concrete goals will be achieved.

It is interesting to note that in our experiences with the elderly we did see leadership emerge. When a social group worker led mental health education discussion groups within a social work agency, staff observed and reported carry-over into other areas of program, and into other aspects of the members' daily lives.

Experience in mental health education and social group work has also helped to clarify the ways in which professional group leadership can be most effective. From its inception, social group work has insisted on the need for a democratic framework if it was to attain its goals. It has never really shifted or modified this point of view.

After many years of experimenting, however, it is now largely agreed that in parent group education, the leader's function is to help the group members extend their knowledge, by learning either from the experiences of other parents, from information provided by the leader as required, or from their own sharpened recognition of factors which up to now have been only partly thought through. The leader serves as expediter, as discussion guide, and as resource person, where necessary, but always within the framework of the discussion that develops as group members strive to meet their current needs at their own level.

As this definition makes clear, what has now emerged is a difficult but important distinction between the authoritarian leader who *tells*, and the laissez-faire leader who lets everyone make his own guesses. On the one hand, we have the basic premise that learning in the mental health field has more to do with attitudes than facts. This point of view was expressed by a teacher who said, "My students are always trying to find simple answers, but I don't teach simple answers; I teach attitudes." On the other hand, we also recognize and celebrate the importance of intellectual pursuit, of the broadening of perspectives through new information, so aptly expressed by Oliver Wendell Holmes: "A man's mind stretched by a new idea can never go back to its original dimensions." By providing information as well as influencing attitudes, the mental health education discussion group helps its members recognize and attempt to meet their own individual problems in their own individual ways.

CHAPTER TWO

What People Discuss:
Practical Concerns

The subjects that people will discuss when given the opportunity to express themselves freely cover a wide range. Mere acquaintances usually stick to matters of the moment—sports, current events, politics, today's newspaper. But when the same group meets regularly week after week, people get to know one another quite well. Then, when there is understanding, permissive leadership, more fundamental concerns tend to emerge. These may vary somewhat, according to the backgrounds of the group members, but generally subjects tend to be basic and universal.

Backgrounds of Group Members

The project from which the material in this book was developed took place in an urban setting. The participants were primarily lower-middle-class and working-class in their origins. The average age was in the mid-seventies. The ratio of women to men was about three to one. Most were foreign-born or first generation Americans, but there were also a number of Negroes, mainly from the South. While there were a few special subjects that tended to preoccupy these particular people, we believe that the attitudes they expressed were fairly typical of members of their generation in similar settings in the United States at this time. We feel, therefore, that this material can be of some value to the beginning group leader in helping him to anticipate some of

27

the attitudes that may be expressed when he undertakes his own work with groups of this kind.

Perhaps the attitudes, feelings and opinions of older people that are described here will help the leader feel more comfortable with certain types of subject matter and, allowing for group differences, may at least give him an idea of what to expect. Fundamentally, we hope it will help him to "creep inside the skin" of the aged in our population, and to see through their eyes what old age means in terms of daily living. The burdens for many are tremendous. Yet one cannot help but be struck by their solid recognition of reality, their courage, persistence and hope. Members of the groups we have known did not reveal that they were waiting to die, but rather that they were fighting with all their will to add meaning to their lives and meet the challenges of their age.

Wide Range of Subjects

In these groups, the range of interests was great. It suggested that almost any unselected group of older people can be invited to "stretch their minds" and investigate a myriad of topics, provided the leader is sensitive to what they say and sincerely encourages them to examine matters in depth. In our experience, the topics for discussion that flowed from the members varied from group to group. Yet rarely was there talk simply for its own sake.

In one instance, a member wanted to discuss comparative religions. When the group too quickly concluded that this had nothing to do with them, the leader might have agreed and classed the member as an "intellectual," out of tune with the group, or as a person unwilling to discuss life's more common problems or one who seeks to avoid discussing human relationships. Actually, it developed, the member was seeking answers to questions which affected her own serenity, questions related to life after death.

However unusual a choice of topic seemed at first, the leader always tried to help the group reduce the inherent meaning to fundamentals that were common to all. In this instance, members were helped to see that it was just as "legitimate" for this member to seek group sanction for her unorthodox thoughts about religion as it was for others to seek reassurance that they had been good parents. The leader has a responsibility for being alert to this kind of "hidden agenda" and for helping the group see what is involved for each member as an individual.

Classification of Topics

In our own experience the content of discussions seemed to fall into these classifications:

1) *easily identified, "practical problem" areas,* such as housing, finances, health, employment and retirement

2) *personal relationships,* such as the role of parent and grandparent, friendships and feelings of love, sex and second marriages

3) *more abstract concepts,* such as conformity, hope and happiness, destiny, religion

4) *matters of social organization,* such as their own clubs and centers, their meaning and how they use them

In each of these areas people contributed anecdotes, personal experiences and opinions which expressed their attitudes. Here is a summary of some of the facts and feelings which the group members shared with us:

HOUSING. With time, money, health, friends and family all running out at the same time, so to speak, it is not unusual that the elderly should talk of feeling trapped. Although this feeling comes up in relation to many things, it is significant that among the groups we worked with it found its strongest expression in relation to housing. In a world that values a man by his car, his job, his friends, his club affiliations, his wife's fur coat and his house, his house is often the only thing left to an older person, who nevertheless may still strive to show "who he is" by the same set of values. For such a person, his house is his strongest source of identity. In addition it often stores up memories and holds souvenirs of earlier days with parents, spouses, children, neighbors.

Fortunately, attention to the needs and wants of the elderly is increasing in many public and private agencies. However, we have a long way to go before the social welfare services and opportunities so urgently needed are actually supplied. Members of our groups have seen the changes taking place, but because these changes have been slow, it is difficult for some to believe that their own concerns could possibly be alleviated during their lifetime. In such circumstances, factual information about the history of change and the power of the group play an important part in improving perspective for the future. To be able to say that the public housing allotted to the elderly has risen a certain percentage in the last 15 years; to point out that public housing agencies sometimes involve community groups and prospective tenants in their planning; to have some group members say that they were relocated in their own neighborhoods and now live in cheerful, efficient apartments in projects—this information may not change an individual group member's disappointment with his own substandard housing but it may very well help ease his feeling that he has been abandoned, that he is alone with a problem no one understands, or that he cannot hope for something better. Other members may even provide the impetus for action which could make him reconsider a move to public housing outside his present neighborhood, or help him approach his own neighbors about making his present living situation more acceptable.

Certainly many of our members needed immediate practical help of some kind. As so often happens, there were those who found themselves living alone in apartments once inhabited by full families. Others felt themselves cooped up in furnished rooms or one-room apartments and spoke of "falling out of the bed into the kitchen sink." Still others had substandard apartments with bathtubs in the kitchen and similar primitive conditions. One 82-year-old was on the fourth floor in a building with no elevator. Ironically, those whose apartments were too large for them found that smaller apartments, more conveniently arranged and easier to maintain, were available only at higher rentals and often in other parts of town. And the thought of moving to a new neighborhood was seen, at least at first, as a change that would make them feel lost and isolated. Sharing their homes with others—taking roomers or boarders—was a possibility, in theory; but many felt or had found that they could not accept new and unfamiliar people in their homes. Throughout this aspect of their discussions, members stressed the need of human beings at every age to have privacy and equated lack of dignity with lack of privacy.

Many who lived alone admitted that they found it lonely but, despite this, most agreed that living alone is preferable to living with one's children. Few saw moving in with their offspring as a solution to their problems. The worst part of living alone seems to be the solitary mealtimes; many people play the radio or turn on the television to relieve their feeling of isolation. Even when loneliness is not a problem, people living alone seem unanimously to share a common fear— the fear of disablement without ready access to help. The preoccupation of older people with this thought makes it clear that living alone in one's later years, when the possibility of illness is so imminent, cannot be equated with that same state at any other time of life. Perhaps this is why many who live without telephones speak of a telephone not as a convenience or an instrument of socialization, but rather as a protective device for use in emergencies.

DEPENDENCY AND "SLOWING DOWN." Individuals taking part in groups such as these are usually the "physically healthy" aged; that is, they can get around on their own and are capable of independent living. Although many have serious chronic illnesses, often of 20 to 30 years' duration, few consider themselves "sick," because they are not bedridden. As a group they appear to be resigned to chronic illness, as though this is to be expected in the later years. Fears of illness in the elderly center about being incapacitated and permanently bedridden. It was often stated, or implied, that this usually means the true ending of life, probably because two of the things most cherished by the old have to be sacrificed when one is bedridden—independence and one's own place to live.

The teen-ager who fractures a hip in the school football game is assured that he has every chance of a full and speedy recovery; that his parents and friends will come to see him as often as they can; and that when the hospital releases him, he will go home, where his whims will be indulged through a brief convalescence. Back at school, he may be a hero. The same accident befalling a person in his seventies or eighties produces dramatically different results. The chances for a full and speedy recovery are much slimmer. The incident may produce or arouse feelings of guilt and fear within the family which can weaken rather than strengthen the family relationship. The extra financial burdens can be extreme, further complicating distress. Companions to whom the patient previously had easy access may not be able to visit him because of distance or because of the anxiety sometimes provoked by a hospital visit. There is no one waiting at home to spoil him or consider him "glamourous" for having had an accident. Sometimes the home itself no longer exists. Rent money may have been used for medical expenses or, if the member is receiving public assistance, the welfare department may decide that the long period of hospitalization and nursing home care required makes the maintenance of an unused apartment financially unfeasible. The emotional trauma brought about by such disaster frequently produces additional physical trauma and deterioration forestalled by years of independence and self-management. These things can seem to occur all at once.

There are conflicting theories about the older person's wishes for dependency and many which suggest that indeed the elderly become more childlike as the years pass. Our experience with the aged does not support this thinking. True, there are many people with dependent characteristics that the reality pressures of aging can accentuate. But this is not inevitable. What we more often saw was the older person desperately intent on maintaining his independence, who sought in many ways the support that would help him to be unafraid, who wanted to know of opportunities to help himself.

Given this spirit, the general slowing-down of old age was often mentioned by members as hard to accept. Many bemoaned the fact that they couldn't do many of the things they used to. Discussion of the facts often revealed, however, either that they could do them— though at a slower pace—or that actually they were no longer interested. Most often their discontent with themselves was a reflection of the nonaccepting attitudes of people about them. Ours is a youth-centered culture. We still think it a great compliment to say that a person doesn't look his age. The older person who judges himself—his appearance, strength, stamina, speed—by prevailing cultural standards is bound to suffer frustrations.

We felt group discussion helped many members to a more realistic view of their situation. To enumerate and then evaluate the importance of more youthful activities they now considered beyond them— dancing, trips to department stores, entertaining large groups of family, staying up late at night, rushing with chores, and so forth—was to see such activities in a new light. Members often admitted they had had no desire whatever to dance in twenty years. Since they had less money to spend, extended shopping expeditions held no charm—under such conditions wandering around department stores can be frustrating and fatiguing at any age. They could manage small family dinners—if they wanted to. With more free time they had no reason to rush through chores. And since in the company of friends daytime hours were the most enjoyable, many preferred to rise early and were content to retire early as well.

By making a realistic evaluation of the effect of self-defeating pressures, and through the support and encouragement they gave each other, members began to admit that shifting gears was not the problem, but rather trying to meet inappropriate standards by denying the facts of old age. The burden for shaping community attitudes cannot be placed solely upon the elderly, but helping them to understand the reasons for their frustrations in this area and to readjust their activities and self-expectations can perhaps eventually affect community attitudes. At the least, it can offer the individual relief from unrealistic pressures, frequently self-generated.

FINANCES. For the most part members of our groups had been skilled and semiskilled workers in factories and offices. A few were formerly small businessmen. Most of them had experienced a comfortable but economically restricted existence for most of their lives. Their ability to plan and provide for financial independence in old age was limited. In any case, general attention to planned preparation for retirement is a relatively recent phenomenon; until recently, many people simply assumed they would work all their lives or would not last long after they stopped working. Most were so preoccupied with current financial pressures that they could not have saved or invested significantly had they wanted to.

People vividly remembered their first jobs and how much they were paid; the struggle to get ahead and to overcome oppressive working conditions; their desire to "educate the kids" so that their children's lives might be different. How does such an older person adjust to a once-more restricted financial situation? Is he able when necessary to accept help comfortably? Often he will maintain that throughout his life, while he didn't save much, at least he didn't have to ask for anything from others. Even those who did so may deny it, as if to imply that help at an earlier stage was different, because so long as one had earning capacity, help could be considered a loan.

A common attitude among our group members was their reluctance to seek financial aid from their children. Yet many were quite objective and realistic about having had to become "a financial burden." Admittedly this is a subject most people dislike discussing openly, but we saw no cases of aged persons who stated or implied that they expected assistance from their children and were disappointed. (Whatever disappointments in their children members expressed seemed much more concerned with poor basic relationships.) On the other hand, among middle-class suburban groups family conflict not infrequently centers around the younger generation's demands for loans or outright assistance from the older. While this was not an issue in our groups, it can raise many questions when it does occur. If help is given should it be as a loan or an outright gift? Should one save more than a minimum for oneself? Will giving make one's children too dependent? Should one provide a sum substantial enough to jeopardize one's own finances? Money for grandchildren would be another topic for discussion in such areas.

For the aged in groups such as ours another source of financial help is public assistance. Most of the people we saw receiving this aid, although grateful for it, considered it a necessary evil. The fact that public assistance is a tax-supported service, one to which they themselves had contributed and to which they could legitimately lay claim, was not recognized. It was seen as "charity," and these people did not accept it comfortably. This held true to such an extent that many members neither knew nor tried to ascertain the range of resources and special services available to them through the public assistance agency. The welfare agency's pressure on adult children by invoking their legal responsibility to force contributions to the support of aged parents was at times a factor here. Where this had occurred it was seen as embarrassing and demeaning and was sometimes the cause of strained family relationships. Perhaps some of the passivity we noted in recipients of public assistance reflected the feeling that rather than cause anyone possible trouble they would do without.

On the other hand, there was no feeling of stigma expressed about receiving Social Security. This seemed natural and to be expected. Not only is Social Security given in a dignified impersonal way, it is something everyone now plans on. This distinguishes it markedly from public assistance intended only for the indigent.

EMPLOYMENT AND RETIREMENT.   Possibly because the average member in these groups had already been retired for some years and had made some adjustment to this challenge, retirement did not occupy much discussion time. The implications and effects of retirement, however, were often indirectly evident when people talked about loss of prestige and status ("Nobody really cares about you when you're old") and loss of personal identity ("I used to be something. I could say I was a printer. Today I'm nothing."').

Those groups who overtly discussed retirement from work sometimes expressed frustration but could not clearly focus it. Usually, they stressed two things: One, when they had a job, they had a daily routine and felt a greater sense of purposefulness; two, they now had lots of free time available and didn't know how to use it.

Discussion often revealed ambivalence and confusion. Some said, for example, that since they desired more routine, they'd be better off if they could return to their old jobs. However, in discussing what a working life involves, they were the first to say they could no longer tolerate the things that go with it, such as standing in the bus or subway, getting into crowds, the fatigue and responsibility of full employment, having to master new machines, not to mention the problems created by automation.

Many who were actually enjoying the slow pace they described as "loafing" were confused, perhaps even guilty, about accepting it outright. They seemed to feel that they ought to want to work, that such a wish was expected of them, although in essence they did not desire it. No doubt this ambivalence and confusion is largely the result of conflicting social pressures. The same society which may compel retirement or label a person "too old" to get a job somehow rejects the person who does not "produce."

Yet we did meet people in our groups who had managed to take on new roles successfully. Many were enjoying a good part of the free time they now had and were leading purposeful, constructive lives. Both men and women were maintaining themselves independently within their communities, shopping, cooking and cleaning for themselves. They were discovering new interests and pursuing them. They were getting involved as citizens on local and national issues in ways that many had never tried before. Some were developing and using skills of organization and leadership. Some were making new friends, finding time to enjoy grandchildren and gaining from them satisfactions of companionship they never had from their own youngsters.

In these ways they were demonstrating that they had the capacity to change, that they were willing and able to adapt themselves to new styles of life. Despite the fact that in many ways they were more hindered than helped by conditions and attitudes around them, they were going ahead to meet successfully the challenge for which they were so ill prepared.

[CHAPTER THREE]

What People Discuss:
Personal Relationships

Parenthood and Grandparenthood

When discussing their own children, group members often said that they did not feel a lack of love and respect in these relationships but rather a lack of communication and mutual understanding. For example, one woman who lived by herself had complained to her son of being lonely. He responded with a lecture on the blessings of financial security and good health for which she should be thankful. Later in the group discussion, the member repeated the story and said, "Maybe I shouldn't feel sorry for myself, but I *am* lonely. And he just doesn't understand."

Another member, an officer in a day center which she attended regularly and where she had found a male companion, obviously satisfied many needs through this outlet. Yet her daughter had laughed at her and ridiculed the idea of "a man and woman their age" taking cha-cha lessons at the center. The member, deeply hurt and humiliated, said she now mentions nothing of her activities to her daughter. This illustration, incidentally, is typical of the kind that can be woven into a role-playing situation. We did so here in an attempt to help the members develop understanding of their children's attitudes. It was hoped that helping them see things through their children's eyes would foster communication or at least one-sided understanding that would make them less vulnerable to their children's insensitive comments.

Women appeared to have closer relationships with their children and grandchildren than did men. They saw these offspring as their primary sources and outlets for affection and said they preferred to get gratification through family ties than to risk the involvement of new heterosexual relationships.

Male group members, on the other hand, said they did not feel particularly close to their children or grandchildren. They more freely expressed their need for affection from women their own age.

Very few saw their role of grandparent as meaningful and important to the child. Some had grandchildren who lived at great distances from them and whom they saw annually, but many more had grandchildren who lived in suburbs which were not easily accessible and to whose homes they said they waited to be invited. Even when families lived nearby, "waiting for an invitation" was common.

Those members who looked back to their own grandparents as models were, of course, faced with frustrations. Present-day grandparents have different roles, and considerably less control and direct involvement with youngsters. They needed help in understanding the reasons for the development of expert advisers to parents, like Doctors Gesell and Spock, their own children's new knowledge about child-rearing practices, and modern attitudes about discipline.

In all groups where this was discussed, we placed great emphasis upon their love relationship with the grandchildren, since this was an area they could patently enter with ease and comfort, and in which indeed they were experts. Sometimes members would start discussion by saying, "Of course we love our grandchildren, but . . ." as if to minimize the importance of this quality compared to other areas where they felt some inadequacy or frustration. At such times we often contrasted love relationships with grandchildren against other relationships experienced within a lifetime. We attempted to show that there are probably no others in which an adult is free to give so much love without having to feel directly responsible for other aspects of behavior and where the only thing he asks in return is some small measure of recognition. Theirs, we pointed out, was a special gift to offer, and the child who received such love would be immeasurably enriched for all time.

In addition, we focused upon the grandparent's potential role as the family historian, the perpetuator of tradition and ceremony. We helped members recognize that they had meaning not only as individuals but as symbols, as links with the past, providing perspective through which children could begin to see that life, through the family, has endless continuity, neither beginning nor ending with themselves as individuals.

We often pointed out that children would lose a great deal, their lives would be less rich and colorful, if not for grandparents. The many pressures on families often make the grandparent the only member available with the real desire and ability to indulge a young child's curiosity in such simple, unhurried pleasures as a stroll through the dime store, watching fish in a park pond, or playing a game of "pretend."

Many whose grandchildren were of school age or older expressed concern about today's youngsters, not so much about their behavior ("We were no angels either") as about their values. Our population was earlier described as relatively unsophisticated, yet they showed great interest in and awareness of the factors leading to the change in children's attitudes and behavior. Through provocative discussion they concluded that today's manners and morals had to be seen in relation to the "age of violence" in which we live. Some children's unhealthy concept of authority might be related to a lack of respected images, influenced by a father's lack of status or by the limited time he spends in the home.

Family Role and Acculturation

Despite the inherent importance of grandparenthood, most people in actuality expressed a lack of conviction about significant status or respected role in family life. Like a dull pain, this feeling permeated many discussions. Again and again, they spoke of the need to feel important within some familiar social structure. Members expressed both bitterness and bewilderment at being unprepared for their present role and at not having appropriate patterns to follow. For example, once they acknowledged that they had little in the way of special skills or knowledge to contribute to their families, they were at a loss to define for themselves what qualities might be substituted.

As mentioned earlier, they felt that the majority of aged parents were better off living apart from their children. Yet they were deeply affected in many ways by the physical separation of the family. The greater formality which often resulted ("waiting to be invited") reduced opportunities for companionship and the sharing of small family pleasures. This was particularly heightened by changing neighborhood patterns, resulting in isolation, anonymity and insecurity ("Once I knew almost all my neighbors. Now I could die in this apartment and no one would know the difference.").

Foreign-born aged contrasted their own European families with the changing American culture of which they were now a part. They re-examined their reasons for coming to the United States, the hardships endured, and the aspirations they had held for their children. In the process, we pointed out that achievement of these aspirations often required independence and mobility, which encouraged separation. This kind of emphasis helped counteract feelings of guilt by reinforcing the fact that they had *not* been bad parents, they had *not* failed in their task. The effects they were feeling stemmed rather from social and cultural dislocations that were part of America's growing pains.

Incidentally, it is interesting that members tended to feel little compassion for today's immigrants, such as the Puerto Ricans. They were unable to accept that the latter's reasons for migrating could be similar to their own. They minimized the newcomers' struggles and almost seemed to resent that certain new health and welfare measures have eliminated some of the hardships they were themselves forced to cope with. Their own acculturation to the values of American society and their position they had won in it for themselves placed them worlds apart from the newcomers. Thus, in relation to these newcomers, poor housing (which many of them had themselves endured 50 years ago) was seen not so much a serious social problem as a reflection of the immigrants' own inadequacy.

Marriage and Divorce

To help the members better understand the behavior of young people required a long look at factors affecting marriage today.

Understanding awareness of the romanticized preconceptions and lack of preparation that jeopardize the success of marriages was often impressive. Members formulated many of the same ideas that eminent sociologists have expressed, although in simple language based on personal observations rather than on research. But had the members in their own youth been any better prepared than the young people they were discussing? Surely they were as much influenced by the mass media of their time as people are today. Rudolph Valentino was no more typical of husbands in the 1920's than is Rock Hudson forty years later. Members agreed but implied that other factors had balanced this false image. Their familiarity with struggle throughout their early years had helped them learn to cope with difficulties and adapt to change. Somehow, they felt, this had better prepared them to meet the challenges of marriage. They spoke, too, of the strengths often derived from the three-generation family living within one household. When the family extended beyond spouse and children, other adult members could be a source of physical, emotional and financial support. Unlike today's couples, young people in such a situation did not take on, alone, the total responsibilities of a new marriage. Consequently they were spared much of the stress that comes with full responsibility for all shopping, cooking, cleaning and child care.

As for legal changes over the years, many felt that the relative ease with which divorces are obtained makes a mockery of moral commitments in a marriage. There were several who voiced the opinion that marriages are entered into with full cognizance of an "escape clause" and who said they thought divorce laws ought to be more stringent.

Love, Sex, and Marriage in the Later Years

It was not surprising that those people who appeared to be most healthy, emotionally speaking, seemed to have the most positive attitudes about these subjects. They seemed to be less opinionated, less prone to generalizing, more willing to be flexible. These were the people most able to risk personal relationships.

Aside from these differences, there was a marked contrast between the attitudes of those who talked about these things in the abstract, or in anticipation, and those who were actually experiencing them.

LOVE. Those persons not involved in a love relationship with someone of the opposite sex spoke of love in terms of something past which they did not anticipate experiencing ever again. This attitude was accompanied by such remarks as, "Who's looking for that at this age?" "Who needs it?" "I wouldn't want to be bothered anymore." No amount of discussion about love as comprising compassion, understanding, companionship and so on really changed their feeling that love principally meant sex and romantic love. This restricted definition was partially responsible for the feeling that opportunities to give and to receive love were severely limited. That one could really love friends, people in general, nature, music and so forth almost seemed to come as a surprise, as if they had never thought of these as love objects. Despite their original conceptions of love as being wholly romantic, they approached the possibility of this type of love experience with interest.

Group members who were currently involved or had recently been involved in a love relationship spoke differently. They, on the other hand, minimized the romantic aspects of love, and the comfort with this idea is obvious. They talked much more in terms of companionship, consideration and human response. One man, aged 82, who shared a love relationship with a woman he had met at his club, summed up his feelings by saying, "I felt it necessary to have a friend. I felt the need to have someone to take care of and feel concerned about, whether she was going to reciprocate or not."

SEX. This was understandably one of the hardest subjects for groups to discuss. As one might expect, men were often more willing to talk about it than women and were more forthright in their expressions. Not only do the many taboos associated with sex generally make it difficult to talk about, but sex in later years is often associated with lechery, indelicacy and perversion. Therefore, we felt it particularly important to establish a climate of acceptance within which these men could discuss their feelings. Long years of widowhood or maidenhood among women, added to the fact that our society frowns on their being overt aggressors, had caused many of the women in our groups to suppress or sublimate sexual desires. Perhaps it was the freedom usually granted to men as the pursuers that had kept their desires overt and actively alive.

In one group the leader suggested that there were many myths and much confusion about the sexual interests of older people. Since it was often implied that an interest in the opposite sex disappeared in the later years, we wondered if they would agree? One gentleman made his point very clear: "If that was true, I'd room with this fellow sitting next to me instead of looking for a wife!"

In these discussions, providing accurate information was important and did a great deal to allay guilt and confusion. It was helpful for the group to conclude not only that sexual activity is a highly individual matter, but that medical and psychological evidence supports the assumption that it can be a normal part of aging life. We believe it was also helpful for people to realize that staff could support this point of view and recognize this kind of need along with all other aspects of aging.

MARRYING IN LATER YEARS. For obvious reasons, the majority of opinions about marriage were expressed in relation to second marriage. In general, men were more explicit than women in expressing both the desire to remarry and discontent with living alone. The reactions and opinions of both to the matter of marriage, however, were usually in the context of their own status. Once we presented a hypothetical case, describing an elderly man and woman with a great deal in common who were considering marriage. Both were widowed at the time. One was ill; the other had to face the objections of the children. The group was asked what they thought this couple ought to do. People who had not remarried said they ought to remain friends; those who were partners in second marriages said they should rewed. One group that supported only the continuation of the friendship explained their decision this way: Had the couple been wealthy, they would have suggested marriage; in that case, "they could have retired to Florida, told the kids to go to blazes, and lived happily ever after."

As this explanation would suggest, many of the people we met were overburdened with financial problems that were a constant reminder of limitations they had to accept. Their Social Security allowance represented a degree of individual independence not easily surrendered; yet in most instances remarriage would require the women to do just that. For some—men and women both—it seemed that freedom from financial worries would make life so pleasant that all other obstacles would seem minor by comparison. No doubt there is some truth in such thinking. A psychiatrist has pointed out that elderly people who are sick but wealthy have better morale than elderly people who are healthy but poor.*

In discussing our hypothetical case, the fact that the children objected was usually picked up by the groups, and great weight was placed upon this factor. Some felt that children who would stand in the way of a parent's remarriage were selfish and ought not to be considered; but many more made it clear that they could not regard their children so lightly. There were several reasons for this, such as love ties, relationships with grandchildren, financial dependency and security. Various references to the children as advice-givers, decision-makers and so forth indicated that in many instances the parents were dependent upon them now and that reversal of roles was taking place. One man described his own second marriage in relation to this phenomenon by telling how he had brought his intended bride to his chil-

---

* Alvin I. Goldfarb, M.D. Lecture, "Psychologically Speaking," from *Guide Lines for a Good Life in Later Years.* Community Service Society, October 25, 1961.

dren's home for appraisal. Only after they approved did he feel free to marry her.

Second Marriages

Second marriages which were reported as successful were marked by compromise and sharing. One newly married couple, for example, reported that when physical chores such as carrying the laundry to the basement or washing the floors had become too much for the wife, the husband had agreed to add these to his tasks. In this group, a woman married for many years replied that there was "a fat chance" of her husband doing anything like that. "Anyway," she added after a pause, "I don't want him to do those things. That's my job."

In a few instances, group members said they felt it was not right to remarry if one had been happy with a deceased mate, that it was "an insult to their memory." Although the majority disagreed with this proposition, the idea often aroused sufficient discomfort to stifle discussion. As leader, we often found it safer—and even necessary—to advance many of the arguments against such thinking. Our purpose was to support those who disagreed and to try to dispel the guilt of those who agreed, so that the assets and limitations of marriage could be approached more objectively.

Friendship

Comments offered about friendship were usually related to opportunities available within centers and Golden Age Clubs. They were expressed with such feeling, however, that it seems safe to assume they reflected the members' standards for friendships in life outside these organizations as well.

Loneliness and isolation often were mentioned as prime concerns, yet opportunities for friendship which could help overcome such feelings were not pursued. Members did not appear to extend themselves; they preferred to remain on the level of acquaintanceship. The reasons they gave were extremely negative. For example, the chief reason for having a friend—by their description—was to have someone to turn to in time of trouble. Yet they thought the reasons other people wanted friends were tied up with status. A typical comment revealing this opinion was, "When you no longer have money, nobody wants to know you."

Although other discussions had shown they felt thwarted by lack of opportunity to give of themselves, they did not speak of friendship as offering such an opportunity. There was something of an "everyone is out for himself, no one really cares about me, so why should I bother" attitude. Better, they seemed to say, to have just superficial acquaintances and not get involved.

Not all the members of every group felt this way, but this attitude was definite and frequently encountered. It may have arisen, partly at least, from the many unsatisfied needs of these deprived people, who had very little social contact outside the centers where they met. In addition, many had not made solid friendships during their earlier years and were not comfortable trying to develop them at this late stage in life. On the other hand, in comments made at the close of our series, members sometimes reported that they had "made new friends." When an atmosphere is created where the type of person we have described can express his concerns and find his special needs considered, he often can look at his associates with a new sense of appreciation and with compassion as well.

CHAPTER FOUR

What People Discuss: Philosophy and Social Organization

The fact that we observed it to be difficult for some in our groups to conceptualize, does not mean that they never expressed thoughts or opinions about ideas in the abstract. Indeed, when they talked of such matters we were impressed with the kind of wisdom and/or perspective they showed, which indicated their continued ability to adapt to changes in their lives.

Aging

We tried to learn from the members what age they considered to be chronologically old. Their estimates fell somewhere in the late eighties or nineties. Since most were in their seventies, this was not too surprising. We are reminded of the comment of Mrs. M, aged 74. She spoke of having seen a man with a long white beard and white hair during a recent visit to the hospital. "Why, he was *only* 77 and he looked about 90," she said.

Even those in their eighties tended not to think of themselves as old. This term was reserved for the bedridden and the physically dependent. Age not only stressed dependency, but also removal from active, participating life—the inability to continue doing things which they equated with youth.

Conformity

While our groups tended to maintain conformist attitudes on most subjects, it was evident that many were tending to modify some of their lifelong reactions, allowing themselves, perhaps, the luxury of being able to deviate a bit.

For example, there was the 80-year-old lady who began testing out our acceptance of her use of slang. Basically a rather reserved and proper woman, she found mischievous delight in the use of "naughty" expressions she obviously had never dared use before. These were of the order of "gee whiz," "shucks," "for Pete's sake" and the like, but to her each expression was an adventure. The fact that she could use them without rebuff gave her a sense of freedom she had never permitted herself and one which she obviously enjoyed.

This sense of freedom was also evident in some members' observations about religion. Actual church attendance, adherence to ritual and the importance of religion in their lives seemed to be matters they had just begun to think about and to question in new ways. We feel this is worth mentioning because of the widespread generalization that old age brings with it a return to organized religion. As we shall explain later on, there were some specific exceptions to this tendency.

Happiness

Sometimes we introduced this subject by asking members to recall and characterize the happiest times of their lives. On other occasions we might ask what they needed to keep them happy.

Since the definition of happiness can vary with the individual and his time of life, happiness is at best a difficult state to define. Our members did it through examples that were often very tender. They spoke of the years they worked at things they enjoyed doing, of being happy because they were financially independent, busy, and helpful to others. They spoke of happiness during courtship or early married life, distinguished by a sense of fulfillment, peace of mind and fond expectations. They mentioned the freedom from responsibilities that characterized childhood and the joys of feeling loved and protected, of receiving gifts.

These are only a few of the many examples in which two striking factors kept reappearing: first, the association of happiness with periods marked by hope and anticipation and, second, those in which there was involvement in a close relationship with at least one person.

Obviously, these are satisfactions derived from being part of the life stream of existence and, as such, they are less accessible to persons who have withdrawn and retired from life. That happiness was defined in this way by our members is no accident. This point of view, at least in part, stems from our culture, which by and large rejects its aged. They were saying, in essence: "We feel cut off from people and we have little to look forward to. These things make us unhappy."

Hope

The question of hope relates to the definition of happiness among the aged, but our people indicated that the concept of hope is seen in a special way during later years.

At other ages, hope tends to carry the connotation of a future. For example, a little boy hopes to become an Eagle Scout some day, a high school girl hopes she will be invited to next month's prom; a young college student hopes that some day he'll be a famous scientist; a housewife hopes that soon she'll have enough money in that secret fund to reupholster the living room sofa. Our population spoke of hope in different terms. They freely admitted that the past is unchangeable and stated they felt little control over the future, which was often tenuous at best. They explained that in consequence they lived from day to day and their hopes had to come on a daily basis, in small ways. We often wondered, during discussions about the pressures and tensions of the world in general, whether this factor was responsible for their completely ignoring such cosmic problems as the atom bomb, the perils of nuclear testing and the like.

The Discussion Leader and "Hope"

If the discussion leader can see hope in the members' context, he has a great deal to offer. Our people indicated that, for them, hope was dependent on two factors: first, the feeling that one is able to act and, second, the belief that one's actions can in some way be effective in turning expectations into realization. When we talked about the increase in percentage of public housing available for the elderly; the interest of the Federal government in the aging, as reflected in proposed legislation; the extension of services and provisions for the aged in public welfare laws, we were not only providing information but were consciously trying to offer beacons of hope that might serve to enlarge their limited future expectations.

We helped them to become more knowledgeable about available health services and how to get them, as well as about the rights of welfare recipients and how to go about obtaining goods and services. We helped them to arrange a plan, within their clubs, to provide mutual assistance in case of illness. We acquainted them with facilities for summer vacations and encouraged agency staffs to request their boards of directors to establish subsidies that would make possible the use of such facilities. In other words, we tried to help them hope in terms of realistic, limited, practical goals. We also tried to help them gain satisfaction from the kind of hope that motivates people to work for others.

We found that the mental health education series itself tended to stimulate hopefulness. Through it groups were given a chance to identify with a leader whose presence and interest refuted the idea of abandonment, one who maintained a positive optimistic attitude which, in turn, affected members' feelings about themselves. The leader can give love, comfort, support and encouragement to people who are usually in great need of such attentions and this part of his role should not be underestimated.

Memories and the Past

We judge a man by the sum of his achievements throughout a lifetime. What he has been and what he has done are reflected in him in his old age. Still, there is a tendency in others to rebel when an aged person reminisces about his past, as witness remarks like "Old people are always living in the past" or "Old people are always talking about the good old days."

Our population showed the effects of this common attitude. They hesitated to talk about the past because they did not want to be characterized as old people and because they did not want to meet with rejection. Consequently, they were conflicted about this and often criticized one another for being guilty of such behavior.

One week, following a group discussion of this topic, a woman asked if she could reopen the question. She had been so bothered by this group's initial reaction to the topic that she had not been able to listen to its conclusions—which would have given her, at the time, the reassurance she was still seeking. She spoke of the preparation for the birth of her first child. Each article of clothing she bought or made was hung on a line in the new baby's room, in anticipation of its arrival. "It's one of my most precious memories and I like to think about it. Is that wrong?" By this time, others had arrived at some resolution of the conflict through the previous week's clarification. They were obviously moved and were both patient and tender in their support of her plea. They were able to distinguish, however, between using memories for healthy satisfaction or reflection and outright "living in the past." The latter, they recognized, could make one morbid and cripple the ability to change or grow.

By and large, our people had demonstrated a capacity for learning and change. Yet they were inhibited about discussing their yesteryears, feeling that few people were interested. They needed help and encouragement to talk about the richness of their past, to be reassured that it had not all been in vain, and without joy or love. It took them time to realize the vast cavalcade they had seen and experienced: humor and pathos in human relations; social and scientific change all about them.

One of our most heartwarming sessions was a discussion by some foreign-born members of their early impressions of America and the things they remembered about life in New York City in the first quarter of this century. No book or museum could ever tell such stories in quite the same way. They spoke, for example, of their appreciation at being given refreshments on arrival at Ellis Island; the bewilderment of being lost in New York the first day they dared take a walk during a lunch hour; the confusion of life in a boardinghouse at the age of 14; the pride of buying one's first blue serge suit with one's own money. They told of the coachmen in stovepipe hats driving carriages of elegantly dressed ladies past their homes near the docks and recalled such dramatic events as the Triangle Shirt factory fire.

It was one thing to acknowledge the validity and the substance of their memories, another to help them use these memories appropriately; that is, in situations in which they would not be rebuffed. Emphasis was therefore given to sharing these treasures with their grandchildren or the children of friends. One group decided to work on a project with the local public school, wherein the members might serve as resource people in discussions of early modes of transportation in New York City, talks about early communication media and the like. One group had so much fun reminiscing they decided to write a column in their club newspaper for the enjoyment of the total membership. One man became so stimulated by his memories that he started writing stories about his early work experiences, how he met his wife, the places they had lived and so forth. He sent his writings to his grandchildren, whom he seldom saw because they lived some distance away.

To deny a man his memories, or the value of them, is in a sense to deny that his life had meaning or importance. For the aged, who have the largest part of their lives behind them, this has particular pertinence. All of us who work with them and are concerned with their mental health need to be especially cognizant of the significance of their past for their self-esteem and of their need to reassure themselves through recollection of past knowledge and experience.

Destiny and Religion

The attitudes of our population toward religion covered a wide range and were greatly tempered by the complexities of daily living. When we spoke of the Ten Commandments, for example, all members acknowledged them as a fine set of moral standards but spoke also of the difficulties of leading a perfect life. They were well aware of man's frailty and showed a good deal of compassion and tolerance for human weakness.

A minority unquestioningly believed in a Supreme Being, One Who makes all the big decisions for the individual, makes them all for the best, and provides the promise of an afterlife. Such firm belief was a great source of comfort which the other group members at times appeared to envy. Even those who said they felt they had to depend upon their own will and make their own choices seemed to be searching for some Power with which to share their burdens. This manifested itself in a variety of questions about predestination, astrology, reincarnation, luck and so forth.

A large majority of the religionists, as well as the less rigorous conformists, spoke of diminishing adherence to ritual. No doubt the status of their family life—especially separation from the younger generations —and the urban context in which they lived tended to bring this about. The rituals observed as part of family life can become less meaningful when there is little or no family with which to share them. This is also true when one is no longer directly responsible for influencing the young in a certain way.

In the small towns of an earlier day, many persons attended the same house of worship all their lives and knew the minister and others in the congregation intimately. Today, however, especially in cities, where there is much mobility and population shift, stable congregations are rare. Either the composition changes, or the congregation diminishes to such an extent that it moves to another location. While many members still enjoyed Sunday church attendance, there was a lack of identification with a particular church. Because of such community changes, the realities of carfare costs, and the hardships of public transportation, many members said they attended the church with the most convenient location regardless of denomination. These same population shifts made many people strangers in their own neighborhoods, so that they were free of the social pressures which might have affected church attendance in other years. They went to church now if and when they felt like it.

One of the groups had a large percentage of Negroes, whose attitudes differed markedly from others expressed. They all spoke very warmly of the church, were closely identified with it, and made its importance in their lives very clear. For example, they spoke frequently of the Lord and of biblical teachings in discussions that touched in any way upon morality, such as those on family life, love, friendship, prejudice and the like. It was our feeling that the churchgoing Negro members held to religion not only as a belief but as a way of life, that it had become an integral part of their thinking and a specific guide to attitudes and actions.

Their Own Clubs and Centers

If anyone ever doubted the validity of senior citizens' clubs and centers, they would have only to speak with the members to resolve any questions. Time and again, the members of our groups expressed their gratitude—regardless of the auspices, the physical plant, the kinds of services offered, or the composition of membership within their clubs. One club consisted of two small basement rooms badly in need of paint, dark, dingy, poorly furnished and approached down precarious steps leading through a narrow alley. It impressed us as rather sad and wanting, yet members who had been coming there for years never referred during the discussion series to the inadequacies and perils of their surroundings. The human contacts, the sense of belonging, a place to go each day—these matters took priority in their minds.

Their loyalty and devotion to the staff was intense—not surprising, since the feeling was usually mutual. Day after day, staffs provided patience, understanding, affection and service, often under great stress and difficult working conditions, because they cared about the membership. And their members knew it. Mr. M summed up for many what the center meant. A lonely and dejected man once his wife died, he had spent most of his days on a park bench. A friend invited him to come to a center and he soon became an active member. As he put it, "When I first came here I was 150 years old. Now I feel like I'm 16 again."

Not only are many older people without the routines usually provided by homemaking and employment, but the absence of family also means that the home is no longer the center of leisure and entertainment. As a means of filling these needs alone, the importance of centers and clubs cannot be underestimated. They serve in other important ways, too. Many members were discovering for the first time in their lives interests, skills and capacities for involvement they didn't know they had. This was particularly evident in the areas of citizenship and local government. The centers provided the means, the encouragement and the information these beginners needed to become engaged in such activities.

Members were not entirely without criticism of their centers, however, and seemed most sensitive to those attitudes in staff members and others which ran counter to the many positive attitudes previously mentioned. They were readily aware of any denial of democratic participation and self-determination, and if the staff, even inadvertently or unconsciously, limited their rights and opportunities, they resented it. And said so in group meetings.

They resented, too, having to become involved in activity for its own sake or in projects that did not come to a logical, well-ordered conclusion. This criticism was angrily expressed by a man whose pottery pieces had never been fired. The center owned a kiln but some administrative mix-up had prevented the use of it. The member was a skilled craftsman who took pride in his work. He said that crafts under such conditions were a farce and felt that they should not be offered if facilities were inadequate.

Others were critical of instructors for praising—or accepting for bazaars—crafts pieces which did not measure up to their own standards. We recognized that the instructors were well intentioned in their efforts to lend support and encouragement. On the other hand, when one sees how reality-oriented the elderly are in other aspects of life, one must question the advisability of any effort to protect them that ignores their sense of realism and integrity to standards.

All in all, we felt they were making a plea for their dignity and self-respect by asking that the standards of acceptance which apply to all adults not be lowered for them.

CHAPTER FIVE

Concepts and Goals in Working
with the Aged in Groups

Because the psychological adjustments demanded by retirement, widowhood, and aging in general are considerable, many men and women in their later years find themselves frequently, often needlessly, bewildered and distressed as they struggle to cope with a never-ceasing series of changes in their lives. If this widespread situation is to be eased, all the knowledge and skills developed by mental health specialists in group work of various kinds must be brought to bear specifically on program planning and direct services for the aging.

A real challenge! Where do we begin? What kinds of services can be most useful in helping older persons accept emotional, physical and social changes? How can their later years be made fruitful, rewarding and fulfilling? What new and better ways can we employ to help each individual develop the insights, strengths and skills he needs to find his own meaning and purpose? The mental health education discussion group is one tool that can play a significant role in answering some of these questions.

Some Concepts

Controversy has been keen over differences in purpose and practice among professional group workers in the mental health field. The specialty of mental health work with which we are concerned (mental health education) concentrates primarily on prevention. The individuals to whom it is geared are persons healthy enough in their social relationships to function adequately in reality situations. To preserve and foster this social health, however, they may need help in identifying and using their strengths. Rather than focus on problem areas, the approach we chose tried to strengthen the individual's resources for health, to enrich and reinforce rather than explore deeply and change radically.

Although working with the aged in groups is still very much in the experimental stages, its potential usefulness seems very great, particularly in clubs and centers where the elderly congregate naturally. For a variety of reasons, mental health education groups can be easily formed in such settings: Members know each other and often have common needs and interests. Centers are usually neighborhood-based and groups tend to have a homogeneous quality. The organizational structure often permits progress made by individual members and the group as a whole to be carried over into other activities.

Setting up such groups can be relatively simple, then. But if the groups are to succeed in their purpose, those responsible must be clear on their principles and goals and have at least general guidelines for procedure. During our two-year demonstration project we found that we drew upon the general concepts already established in mental health and family life education, modifying these concepts as needed. With this as a foundation, the following principles for working with older people were developed. These gave direction to our goals.

Goals

1) We would support the personality strengths of our group members, encouraging their feelings of self-worth and self-acceptance. We would concern ourselves with promoting self-mastery, encouraging each group member to take action on his own behalf and work to control his own experiences. We would hope, through this work, to lead each individual toward an increased appreciation of his own inner resources, a sense of personal competence, a release of spontaneity and creativity.

2) We would use in our work the kinds of methods and the type of content that would both support and challenge, inform and inspire.

3) The leader would attempt to make the group experience pleasurable as well as significant. In a successful session, members would share in enjoyment of the leader and of each other. There would be laughter, provocative stories and lively human illustrations to help members experience the satisfactions of listening and sharing. By developing resources within the group, interest would be heightened and maintained.

4) To keep the focus on health and strength, we would be careful in coping with the content of the sessions. We would handle only conscious material, avoiding any temptation to interpret or manipulate unconscious or pathological elements. While there is much relief and comfort in sharing, our groups were not planned to be the media for pursuing in detail deeply personal feelings or highly emotional experiences. Any such impulses, we determined, would be carefully controlled. Such handling is reassuring to most group members and helps the more volatile ones see what is, and is not, appropriate in group sessions.

5) We would attempt, by providing information and interpretation, to broaden the group members' perspectives about behavior appropriate to their changing roles in later life. We would trust the group to use what was relevant and to discard what might be threatening or inappropriate.

6) We would help group members to see their individual reactions and concerns in the broader context of universal human experience, both to increase their understanding of human behavior and to provide the necessary reassurance of shared feelings and concerns.

7) The leader would help the group become more flexible in its ability to tolerate, accept—even relish and enjoy—individual differences, differences not only in verbal expression but also in the wide range of ways men and women participate in a group. The timid, the shy, the person who reveals his feelings by facial expression or body movement, can be as significant to the group experience as the person who is verbally facile. The development of mutual respect and trust among all group members would be a primary goal.

8) The leader would encourage self-questioning in relation to the

members' challenging and questioning of each other. As differences in opinion and experience emerged, an attempt would be made to use these various responses for a greater appreciation and awareness of the valid, indeed essential, differences in people. In addition to stimulating recognition of individual differences, where appropriate we would encourage the recognition of realistic differences among persons as members of ethnic, racial and even neighborhood groups.

9) We would try to help each member find his special place within the group, so that the richness and variety such differences add would become apparent both to the individual members and to the group as a whole.

10) We would try to help group members improve their ability to communicate their feelings to others and develop an increasing capacity to relate warmly to others.

11) We would hope to demonstrate that behavior is motivated and has meaning.

12) We would encourage an awareness that thinking and feeling, "heart and head" together, affect every aspect of existence; that the intellectual and emotional aspects of living are inseparable. We would provide information and ideas intended to encourage the changing of feelings, attitudes and insights. The members' everyday experiences of living would provide us with the content.

13) We would hope to help members realize that it is possible to recognize and accept even unpleasant feelings in themselves and others, yet limit the behavior such feelings might inspire.

14) Along with helping the members develop in heart and mind, the leader would be ready to help them move to other levels if they wished to do so—to use their new ideas and the stimulus of their group experience to expand into other areas of study and into action of one sort or another.

In actual contact with groups of aged persons, these precepts were subjected to the severe test of direct application. In many ways they were more than vindicated. The groups developed their own special character; individuals were moved and touched by one another. There was laughter and sadness and an earnest seeking for meaning. In helping others, each member found new learning, personal enrichment and inspiration—an ever-deepening sense of the inherent strength and dignity of the human person.

Special Considerations

Work with the aged based on the goals and principles set forth here should carry promise of success in any setting and with members of any social or economic group, given the basic emotional health required for this type of education. In practice, however, the kinds of elderly persons most likely to be reached through groups in urban centers such as those in which we worked share certain characteristics which must be considered if the fullest benefits of such efforts are to be achieved.

a) The aged at this time, especially those in large cities, tend to have less formal education than younger persons, and many are of foreign origin. These and other factors may tend to handicap their efforts to express themselves clearly and keenly on vital but subtle matters of opinion and feeling. Experienced discussion leaders may find that the participants' level of approach and choice of language may differ from those of more sophisticated groups. But the content may well be just as deep and meaningful.

b) Similarly, today's aged are not, and never have been, given to "psychiatrizing." Generally accepted psychological theories about human behavior which, intellectualized and verbalized, are so much a part of the thinking and conversation of younger age groups, are often alien to the aged. In situations where other groups might be stimulated by probing, the elderly may feel threatened and uncomfortable. Workers with the aged must move accordingly in introducing such concepts. They should be alert to, and even more important, ready to accept without concern the resistance—and even the hostility—that any reference to these "new-fangled notions" may arouse.

c) Because of their lack of prior exposure to this type of education and help, the aged are unlikely at first to see the group as a place where one seeks answers to problems. They may come initially because a friend invited them or because they are curious about the leader.

They may not think at all in terms of the group's potential personal value to them or their friends.

d) This lack of clarity about purpose may mean that three or four sessions will pass before the elderly members really understand what the group is all about. However, their rambling during these early sessions should not be taken as a sign of disorientation. It often represents the beginning of participation, a sending out of feelers to test and judge the acceptance which the group conveys. Often it is a necessary preliminary before the naïve individual develops the ability to make clear, concise comments. These early sessions, therefore, are not wasted time. Nevertheless, the leader should take every reasonable opportunity to offer conscious, repetitive clarification of the group's purposes and goals.

e) Once the group's purpose is understood and real discussion begins, the elderly are likely to want to concentrate first on consideration of day-to-day problems, concerns of an immediate and practical nature. Burdened by reality pressures seen in the context of a limited future, they may want to talk at length about factual details of housing, health care and finances. Not until problems such as these have been considered are they apt to become interested in discussing interpersonal relations and their own feelings and reactions.

f) Once a climate of free discussions has been established, however, a complication may arise. Individuals typically will want to talk about themselves, yet show intolerance of others who do the same thing. Emotionally deprived persons, seldom exposed to the kind of opportunity for communication which these groups provide, will—understandably—need time to realize that discussion requires give-and-take; that their needs can be met without being the center of attention.

Applicability

These comments are of course based on observations of the people with whom we worked: men and women representative of the majority found in New York City centers and clubs for the elderly. Although there are certain to be exceptions and regional differences, it seems likely that these comments would be equally applicable to aging persons of similar educational background in any urban centers, and in a good number of smaller communities as well. In considering this matter of "education," however, we must distinguish between the knowledge gained from formal training and the wisdom derived from more than half a century of life experiences. Despite their lack of sophistication, group members repeatedly demonstrated the ability to "look life square in the eye," to examine, explore and learn. It is upon this foundation that we built our work with the aged.

[CHAPTER SIX]

Qualifications and Role
of the Leader

The Leader Himself

Anyone who works with the aged, in whatever capacity, has to be able to tolerate a continual and constant awareness of the often painful realities of the later years. He must be able to accept and understand the meaning of loneliness, illness, widowhood, gradually decreasing physical strength and, finally, the full impact of the meaning of mortality.

People who voluntarily enter the field of working with our elderly citizens, if they are to be successful, must not make claims on those with whom they work. They cannot say, "If I help you, you must reward me by living long, being happy and healthy." No such expectation is feasible and the wise worker knows this. He must therefore be someone who believes that life at any age can have value and that it is as important to help people fulfill themselves and continue the search for personal identity toward the end of life as it is in earlier years. He must feel that helping older people achieve a sense of purpose and fulfillment can be significant and gratifying. He must recognize the vital importance of living out all the days of one's life as creatively as possible.

We can make a number of assumptions about most of the people who work in a dedicated way in this field. They are people capable of empathy and compassion; people with a willingness to listen. They have hope and courage and a positive approach to life. As in any field, a small minority undoubtedly have less positive reasons for their choice. Some may prefer being surrounded by the elderly because it helps them maintain a feeling of youth and competent independence. They may relish being in the driver's seat and, with the sense of power this provides, strive to control others who in one way or another appear more in need of help than they. However, the occasional presence of individuals of this type is no more a problem in working with the aged than in any other field. Actually, there is not too much to attract them. Because the work often can be discouraging and difficult and its long-range gratifications limited, its rewards are of necessity in the activity itself. Therefore it attracts most strongly those who really want to give, who want to understand, who are capable of dedicated, unconditional devotion to those with whom they work.

And that is a mighty good beginning for a discussion leader! In addition to this general orientation to life, most staff members have some understanding of the dynamics of behavior, personality formation and development. Those who have made this information a real part of themselves and use it simply and spontaneously, without self-dramatization, are the most likely to succeed in leading mental health discussion groups. Those who, intrigued with psychodynamics and technical jargon, feel impelled to probe, to analyze and to make sweeping "interpretations" are not really suited to the type of work we are describing. The center staff member—even with little technical training—who is sensitive and observant, kind and responsive, may well do a better job than the recently trained worker who has been too involved studying theory to learn enough about himself and others in face-to-face working relationships.

Another important qualification, and one possessed by many persons even without formal training, is knowledge about the social and cultural forces which motivate and influence the lives of people. Cultural and ethnic differences, social pressures and attitudes, economics and politics—all of these influence the lives of the elderly in almost every aspect. All are areas that the leader of a discussion group must be concerned about. We have found that the average experienced worker, regardless of training, usually knows more about all this than he realizes.

There is one area, however, in which experience and training are more likely to be lacking. Even among professionally trained people knowledge and experience with group dynamics and group process are still rare. Persons who have worked primarily in a clinical situation or who have concentrated most of their efforts on the activity aspects of group work have had little opportunity to develop skill in this specialized area.

However, the group discussion method has proved so useful in many areas and demand for it grows so steadily that more and more people are now seeking to develop the particular leadership skills called for: caseworkers, nurses, psychotherapists—even PTA program chairmen in the schools.

Some training centers are available. For example, the Child Study Association of America has been training members of many auxiliary professional groups in discussion techniques. But actual experience is a good teacher, too. Leadership skill can be developed through practice by many who, if they are generally competent in human relationships, will also become increasingly competent in group discussion leadership, provided they keep in mind the basic principles, methods and limitations we are presenting here.

The Leader's Attitude

It is helpful to the beginner to have some supervision and consultation at first, but if this is not available, a do-it-yourself approach to learning can often be very effective. Success at self-education, however, demands trust in the basic health and integrity of other people and a kind of basic honesty with oneself. It requires the ability to be spontaneous and direct, the strength to make a frank examination of what one does, to face one's mistakes and to learn from them. Also vital is the ability to accept oneself as having not only strengths, but limitations as well. This connotes realistic and mature appraisal.

An individual with this kind of clear-eyed view of himself conveys an air of self-assurance and relaxed security which in turn establishes him as a dependable leadership figure in the eyes of a group regardless of his degree of technical knowledge. Such self-awareness also increases the individual's ability to appreciate the meaning and effect of his own behavior on others. When a goal has been established, this willingness on the leader's part to look clearly at his own thoughts and deeds makes it possible to "shift gears," to be flexible, and to make whatever personal modifications may be necessary to insure achievement of that goal.

During the course of group meetings, many points are raised which involve examination by members of their own sense of values—for example, acceptance of new neighbors who represent an unfamiliar minority group. It is not necessary that the leader and the members have the same set of values, but it is important that the leader be viewed as someone with sound, positive values and honest convictions which others can use in testing and evaluating their own. Rather than impose his thinking on others, the leader sets a tone and an example for members to emulate if they choose. His healthy approach to people and situations, the competent way he handles his own responsibilities and tasks, suggest stability, maturity, reality and good judgment. Thus, just by being the person he is, he serves as a source of moral identification to members.

Another important quality of leadership is a healthy respect for learning free of stereotypes and myths such as "You can't teach an old dog new tricks." With the help of a leader capable of building rapport, developing motivation and presenting meaningful material, any older person of normal capacity can learn, and grow in the process.

Along with these established qualities and attitudes, a final qualification should be mentioned—flexibility. The leader must be one who recognizes from the start that there are few absolutes in the area of human relationships, few solely acceptable ways of coping or reacting. It is not enough to acknowledge this intellectually; the leader must communicate this belief to group members through his own warmth, acceptance, flexibility and humor. The members must feel certain that the leader will not be judging or "diagnosing" them if they are to feel free to express honest feelings and opinions.

Individual Differences

It follows that if the leader allows for individual differences, then he must establish a climate of freedom in which the individual can consider and explore the possibilities of different choices of behavior while attempting to choose the one most suitable for him in a particular situation. This permissive, accepting climate is particularly important if the leader hopes to help members modify attitudes or adopt new ideas. Ideas and attitudes do not exist in a vacuum. Developing a really new point of view demands a reorganization of all the ideas, attitudes and values related to the old one. A person must feel it psychologically safe to discuss his doubts and defend his old opinions before he can open his mind to new ones.

Although, as pointed out, the leader should be a stable, mature person, a certain amount of anxiety in the leader is to be expected and is understandable. It is inherent in many helping situations. Different backgrounds, interest and training make it possible for individuals to function well in some professional settings and not in others. Feeling some degree of anxiety related to the nature of one's job or the problems it involves is therefore not unusual or necessarily bad. However, it can become a problem for a worker with the aged if he is unaware of how his work affects him or is unwilling to examine or modify attitudes which might interfere with his work. For example, he might attempt to overcome his anxiety by acting in an excessively controlling way. Or he might tend to regard the members psychologically as "infants," thus denying their adult problems and their own ability to do something about them. Or he may go to the other extreme. His unwillingness to accept them as being aged may cause him to program as he might for other groups, without attention to their special needs.

Learning To Listen

One of the most important and often difficult tasks confronting the leader is that of listening. We are speaking now of the trained and sensitive listening which enables one to detect pertinent material and to be aware of any "hidden agenda." Not only does the skilled leader react to certain spoken words, but he helps group members to hear that which has the greatest possibility of affecting them.

As he becomes more accustomed to listening, it becomes easier for the leader to keep in mind the substance and interrelatedness of each week's discussions, in addition to the general purposes of the on-going discussion. Material previously shared and digested usually has an effect upon the current conversation, and in order to help the series "hang together," the leader consciously points to past facts and previous conclusions whenever it is appropriate to do so.

In addition to guiding the discussion and providing continuity, the leader also helps the group increase its powers of critical thinking; helps them distinguish between fact and opinion. Suppose, for example, in a discussion of dissatisfaction with housing conditions, someone in the group says, "No one cares about the elderly; they are the last to be considered," and presents a pessimistic picture with which the group concurs.

The leader may help the group to think actively (a) by giving direct factual information which may raise questions about the statement and provide some hope; (b) by challenging generalizations which cannot be supported; (c) by helping the members to see their problems as applicable to many age groups rather than unique to themselves. There are many possibilities, depending on the problem. The leader must always be aware that he is aiming not only for lively discussion in which there is good involvement, but for thoughtful discussion as well. His role is that of helping the group to "see," so that it may then find its own answers to questions. The exploration of ideas thus becomes meaningful and lasting.

Thoughts like "No one will ever know what I'm going through" or "No one really understands how much I'm suffering" are not unusual for some persons to have in the later years. Discussion groups with a mental health education focus are excellent places to help such persons feel less isolated and better understood. Toward this end, the leader makes use of the fact that feelings surrounding any incident, ranging from mild disappointment to despair, have been experienced by every member at one time or another. Even though a particular incident raised may not be within the experience of the leader or other group members, the accompanying feelings are universal. The leader may thus permit members to lend whatever understanding and support they can to one another. He will not expect all members to agree on the acceptability of others' behavior—such things as deliberate malice toward a son or daughter-in-law or using physical force on a grand-child may seem understandably reprehensible to many—but he may call attention to the fact that all have experienced similar emotions. Such common feelings as anger, jealousy, rejection, abandonment and the like have been felt by everyone at some time, justifiably or otherwise, and recognizing this helps establish bonds of feeling among the members. In this way, the leader helps the group set the stage for further communication and may help all members deepen their insight and understanding of behavior.

Maintaining the Leader's Role

It is important that group members see the leader as someone distinct and special. Like the keystone in an arch, insignificant by itself, he completes the structure of the group and is vital to its unity.

How does the leader help the group to see him in this way?

a) *He is a part of the group but not a member* and he should not want to be one. However hard the members may seem to be trying to draw him into the group, the leader, to function successfully, must remain separate. The members need to see him as a knowledgeable authority to whom they may turn for guidance, support and protection. His own values have to be maintained and communicated. It is his very difference and objectivity that bring perspective and make him so valuable.

b) *The group leader should consciously try to develop natural leadership among the members.* It is healthy and logical for indigenous leadership to emerge. It signifies that a member's potential has been released, thus allowing him to assume responsibility of one sort or another.

This does not lessen the leader's strength in the eyes of the group; it rather affirms the fact that he sincerely trusts the members to help one another, to handle responsibilities alone, and to make use of opportunities when they meet them.

c) *The leader helps the group understand that he is an authority but is not omniscient.* If his approach is honest he can freely admit without loss of face that there is knowledge he does not have. For example, a group may expect easy, simple answers. ("You're the expert," some member may declare. "Tell us if it's a good idea for older people to get married again.")

Sometimes the group wants information on specific topics such as medicine, insurance or local history which the leader doesn't have. In spite of possible momentary annoyance or disappointment at not having their questions answered, the group will continue to respect the leader's ability if the material he does share with them reflects real competence and knowledge. In areas where he does not have specific knowledge, he should concentrate on the concern behind the question, in order to determine whether members actually want specific information, which he might help or encourage them to obtain, or whether they simply want reassurance and support.

When Individual Problems Arise

When the leader becomes aware that a member is asking for help which the group cannot give him and which is best offered by a specialist within or without the agency setting, clarity is needed about the respective roles of the group leader and the specialist. If the group leader and the agency specialist (social caseworker, referral worker, counselor, and so forth) both try to function as the helping person, the duplication is liable to cause a variety of unfortunate consequences —staff animosity, confusing advice for the client, and ineffective service. In such situations, therefore, the group leader should proceed cautiously, listening briefly to a member's problems, then directing him to the appropriate source of help within or outside the agency. The leader then can aid the specialist by alerting him and providing some background on the individual's particular concern.

For example, a member might be contemplating application for public assistance but fear of going alone to the district welfare center might be immobilizing her. Learning of this, the group leader would be wise to steer the hesitant member back to the person within the agency who had first discussed the matter with her. Thus he would avoid interfering in what had been done to prepare the client thus far and would make it possible for the referral worker to reevaluate the details of his plan by adding the important facts about the member's feeling of timidity and hesitation.

If there is no source of help for a member's special problem within the agency, then the group leader should assume responsibility for seeing that the troubled member is referred elsewhere. The leader may do this himself or through a staff person who will act as liaison between the member and the source of help.

In cases where the group leader is a member of the agency staff, he may wear two hats appropriately and effectively; that is, be both group leader and individual counselor. The structure within the organization will dictate the role of the leader in regard to individual counseling. Generally, however, awareness of channels and clarification of roles will result in more effective help and will enable the leader to invest his energies in appropriate and fulfilling tasks.

Record-keeping

As a leader becomes more experienced and expert, both the volume and the nature of his records will change. For the person beginning in this field, however, records can be a great source of help if he understands what and why to record and how to use the material.

Keeping records of each group meeting is to be encouraged. It is important for the purposes of (a) learning (b) evaluation (c) maintaining continuity (d) determining future focus (e) supervision and (f) teaching. The record need not be detailed or complicated. It might be regarded simply as a useful arm of the discussion group. Without it the group could function but would suffer a disability, so to speak.

What should the leader include in the record? How does he know what is important and what is superfluous? He might think about describing the content, the general level of involvement, group tone and morale, indications of individual participation and growth, and in-stances revealing his own strengths and weaknesses. He should try to keep the record simple and brief. It is his own tool and should be adapted to his and the agency's needs.

In examining and reexamining this material, the leader becomes acquainted with the individual needs of the members, the ways in which he can help them develop, and the special focus they seem to require. Records help the leader to appraise his approach and rapport with the group, evaluate the achievements of group goals and, through study, prevent him from making the same mistakes twice.

When should the record be written? When does it prove most help-ful? If it is to serve the purposes set forth here, it will have to be written up regularly during the lifetime of the group, and fairly soon after the session is concluded. Only thus can it serve as an instru-ment through which the leader may enhance this particular group experience. Experiences recorded once an entire group series ends, however, are valuable teaching tools for other leaders and other agency staffs.

Summary

In this chapter we have recognized that the role and qualifications of a group leader can be demanding. To do his job well, the leader should be a mature and stable person, with special qualities of accept-ance and flexibility and having sound knowledge of human behavior and group process. He must realize that learning can take place at any age. During a meeting he must know how to listen, how to keep the content relevant, how to be accepted yet not "join" the group as a member, how to develop leadership within the group. He helps the group to learn from information and through increasing their powers of critical thinking. He teaches himself and perhaps others through the study of his records. He helps the troubled member get to the appropriate source of help.

In essence, the leader in asking a group to share its concerns, its hopes and disillusionments must be able to offer something in return. He must offer a degree of skill, knowledge and compassion without which there can be no emotional growth and change. In meeting this challenge, the qualities of warmth, self-confidence, concern and spontaneity which emerge help establish him as a responsible agent and a positive force for growth.

CHAPTER SEVEN

The New Leader and the New Group

In the Beginning

Anyone planning to take on the responsibilities of leader for the type of group we've been discussing is likely to feel the proverbial "butterflies in the midsection" as time for the first session approaches. Will the group like me? Can I really get them talking? What if I make a mistake? Questions like these are natural—the answers revolve around the leader himself. This chapter, then, will be addressed directly to the prospective leader—you!

Experienced leaders have found that during the first go-round, it can be very helpful to focus one's thinking on the group rather than on oneself. Try to visualize how *they* see you, your dress, your manner, your physical appearance. If you are middle-aged or younger, you may be seen as a symbol of another generation showing interest in the aging, or perhaps as a spokesman of that generation's ideas. Your youth—comparative or otherwise—might even be cause for mistrust, although this reaction is uncommon and, when present, usually short-lived. You are something different, something new, a change from the ordinary. And you are actually saying to a group that is rarely asked, "Tell me what you feel. . . . I really want to know." These older people are going to find this experience deeply satisfying and will appreciate you for making it possible. Thus, when preparing to begin a group discussion, think more of *them* and less of *yourself*. They will come to the first session prepared to enjoy it and won't be nearly as critical of you as you will be of yourself.

Enjoy Yourself

Speaking of enjoyment, you should feel it, too. There should be a sense of spontaneous pleasure in meeting the group, in seeing personalities emerge, in swapping stories and jokes, in making plans, and in sharing the warmth that comes from the beginning of fellowship. Don't take yourself so seriously that you feel you must always be "studying" the group; don't get the idea that if you find the experience fun you're not being objective enough. Many of the same human responses felt by the members will be felt by you, too. Light, pleasant aspects of the group experience will be something you will both enjoy.

Pitfalls

Even with these advantages in his favor, however, *no* leader can sail through a series without hitting a few channel markers.

From time to time you are going to make mistakes in the way you handle both material and individuals. You should expect this and so should everyone connected with you professionally. Hopefully, you won't make the same mistakes over and over, or as many at the last session of a series as at the outset. Some mistakes or minor errors in judgment are natural if you are a spontaneous human being. Of course you could try to be a walking textbook, to play it safe with all your responses. You might find this easier. But it would be much less meaningful in the long run for all concerned.

Speaking of textbooks, serious difficulties can occur when the leader feels impelled to be overanalytical and to "define," "diagnose" and "interpret" in impressive psychological terminology. But the leader who, in order to avoid sounding pedantic, talks down to the group in an overly simple and elementary way can cause difficulty, too. He insults the members' intelligence, experience and maturity. Initial information can be provided in good, plain English, and you can quickly learn from the group itself what language will be most effective.

Suppose you do make an error in judgment that goes beyond your choice of words. Will it seriously impair the group? We doubt it. For one thing there are usually ways out. You might find, for example, that you have raised a subject for discussion which makes members uncomfortable and unresponsive. Often you can relieve this kind of tension by suggesting that perhaps they would like to discuss this at another time, and focus on something someone said earlier. Later on, the "difficult" subject may be less charged with emotion, if it's worth approaching again.

Remember that your group members almost always are people with an adequate level of emotional health, functioning unprotected within the community. They have survived two World Wars, economic depressions, family tensions, death, illness, labor disputes, forced retirement—the full gamut of life's disappointments and rewards. Enduring a few mistakes in your leadership can seldom cause irreparable harm.

Observers

In some agencies staff observers attend group sessions—to learn or, by supervision, to help the leader with his own learning. If you are new at this, having a staff observer present during your early experiences may make you uncomfortable, particularly if there is any feeling that the observer is concerned with finding fault rather than with learning or teaching. This may be a matter you should discuss with those in charge.

It has been our experience that when an observer remains inconspicuously in the background, his presence has little effect upon the group itself. As the leader, you will have to find the right time to introduce him but after a while, he becomes "a fly on the wall." The leader's spontaneous reactions to content and subject development may be inhibited, however, by his awareness of an observer whose reaction has to be weighed along with that of the group. You may feel you cannot work under such conditions at all. It is not mandatory to have an observer. There are no hard-and-fast rules.

Roadblocks

Be prepared for periods of silence when you or others raise a question or finish a comment. There is nothing "bad" or "wrong" about them. Members may be trying to phrase a response; may be meditating; may feel guilty or uncomfortable about something which touches close to home; or may—because of the way the last remark was phrased—be trying to puzzle out its meaning. After all, aren't there normal periods of silence in every thought-provoking conversation? The only silence that should give cause for concern is that brought on by material so threatening or painful as to immobilize the members. Your own sensitivity to the group will tell you when this is the case. At the start of a series, certainly, such instances should be rare. So, as a new leader meeting a new group, try to remember that what may seem an interminable pause to you seldom appears so to others. Don't be afraid to ride it out. Sometimes, though, it may be the member who made the last remark who is concerned by the silence. At such times, and others, it would be appropriate to rephrase a point, give another example or raise another question. These simple devices can usually recharge a stalled discussion.

The First Session: 14 Pointers

There is no set formula for beginning a session or a series but here are a few suggestions that can be helpful:

1. *Don't Rush Yourself*—Allow plenty of time to arrive on the scene relaxed. If you have to drive, allow for such contingencies as traffic congestion or bad roads. Have a good street map, and perhaps a flashlight. If you are using public transportation, are your directions specific, complete and clear? Though lateness is not necessarily fatal, it certainly is not helpful. Apologies may provide a ready-made approach but it's a negative one at best. One tardy leader driving to meet with her group in a small suburban community left a mailbox at a jaunty angle after a frenzied turn on a dark, narrow street. One would be hard pressed to evaluate her greatest impact on that community.

2. *Room Arrangement*—Check the room setup. Chairs arranged in a circle or in an oval around a long table tend to promote a feeling of informality. Everyone is clearly visible; no one is looking at the back of someone else's head and you are not separated from the group as a lecturer would be. Leaders have often broken the ice by asking some of the early arrivals to help rearrange the furniture.

3. *Get Introduced, if Necessary*—If you are not part of the sponsoring agency's staff, it will probably prove helpful for one of them to take responsibility for assembling the group and introducing you. The stage for beginning is then set with a sense of organization, dignity and relaxation.

4. *Waiting To Start*—In all likelihood, the group will gather slowly, rather than arrive en masse. Should you silently busy yourself with papers until they have all come? Should you feel inhibited about making superficial chitchat? Do you fear that by acting informally you'll get involved with material that ought to come up during a discussion? Don't be leery of acting naturally. You are not the great doctor from Vienna coming with all the answers! You are one adult showing initial curiosity about others whom you are meeting for the first time. As leader of a mental health discussion group, you want to know what they think so that eventually you can affect their attitudes. A feeling of reaching out, of friendliness and informality, should be consciously projected at the outset to help that goal materialize.

5. *Name Names*—Once the meeting begins, the leader will be in the position of recognizing members who want to speak. One of the simplest ways to make people feel respected is to recognize them as individuals, by name. Therefore, learning names as quickly as possible is important. Although there are no rules on the use of first or last names (much depends on precedent) the more formal approach seems better, certainly at the start. Incredible as it seems, we have heard elderly people referred to as "girls and boys," "kids," or "fellas." These terms rarely connote friendliness and informality; more often they are condescending and inappropriate, particularly from an outsider.

Learning names is not too difficult, particularly when, as they often do, people sit in the same seat week after week. One helpful gimmick is to take attendance clockwise or counterclockwise, so that one begins to associate a name with a face in a particular place in the room. By about the third session, almost everyone is known. Thereafter, even in groups as large as 25, taking attendance is no longer needed as a tool for identification.

For other reasons, however, attendance records should still be kept. They can be extremely helpful to the leader in a variety of ways —for recognition, for charting the emergence of a core group, to substantiate a member's interest or lack of interest, to indicate a rise or fall in attendance following the discussion of certain subjects, and so forth. To avoid the feeling of a classroom setup, though, it is well worth the effort to explain briefly why the attendance record is important to you. Perhaps this would also be a good and natural time to point out that regular attendance helps to enrich and enhance the group experience. Acknowledge the fact that some people will naturally drop out and that after a few sessions a core group will remain. Reasonably but firmly make clear, however, that this is not a casual "drop in" program. The discussion room, at least while sessions are in progress, is not a recreation lounge. You might give an idea of the average number of sessions most series usually run and repeat the meeting day, time and place. In other words, outline the structure so that people know what is expected of them and why.

6. *Clarify Purpose and Scope*—As part of this general orientation it will help to mention again just why the group has been formed and, conversely, what it is not going to attempt to do. Some members will need to be reassured that when you talk generally about the feelings and attitudes of people in their later years you don't want to probe their private business or personal secrets. Also, because the word "mental" (in connection with your work in mental health education) is so often associated negatively with phrases like "mental illness," "mentally disturbed," "mental case," and so on, it's not unusual for members to think you might want to "spy on their psyches." Rather than pretend these feelings don't exist, acknowledge them, but then

emphasize the positive purposes of the group in clear, easily under-standable phrases.

Point out that for the first time in history we have so many people living really long lives that the later years of middle life and old age itself have finally been recognized as the important stages they are. With this recognition has come the realization that—by comparison with our knowledge of youngsters and adolescents—we know little about older people, their characteristic behavior and the forces which provoke it. We, "the experts," can't discover these things unaided and that's why we've come to them. (This approach is a long way from being humble; it is straightforwardly true.) We want to explore this phase of life with them, since they are the people living through it. Our purpose, in part, is to learn as much as we can about the various aspects of aging so that future generations, knowing what to expect, will be better prepared. But the experience should prove useful to them individually, as well.

7. *Indicate the Possible Personal Gains*—Continuing along, one might then explain that the members have been asked to participate in this exploration as part of a group in the hope that one person's experiences will help stimulate another's thinking. Their differing reactions will indicate that there is more than one way to meet a situa-tion. It is known that even well past their middle years people can continue to contribute, grow, change, adapt and learn. Perhaps they will learn new things through the sharing of ideas and information. Perhaps some will be relieved to know that others are having the same feelings as themselves. Maybe this whole experience will affect their thinking so much that, when the series is over, they will feel differ-ently about themselves and others. Maybe they will have found some new ways of living life more fully. Perhaps together they can high-light certain concerns and plan to do something about them. Perhaps the conclusions they come to through these discussions will lead to eventual changes in agency and community services and attitudes, affecting others as well as themselves.

8. *Reassure about Participation*—Make it clear that, while there is interest in hearing from each group member, verbal participation will

be on a voluntary basis. Those who wish to sit and listen will have their wish to do so respected; they will not be called upon or forced into any activity before the group.

9. *Suggest Some Subjects To Discuss*—At present there is a lot of conjecture about the concerns of older people. We assume these include housing, the people they live with, their physical health, children and grandchildren, the money they must live on, marriage, religious convictions, the world situation, retirement and even things they seldom discuss with others, like sex and dying. Are they as a group concerned with or interested in talking about these things? Are there good and bad aspects to aging? Do they feel satisfied with this time of life, or are things turning out differently than they expected? Is it possible that new inventions, increased industrialization, automation, changes in city living and so forth have had some effect upon them?

If you put yourself in the group member's place for a moment, surely you'll agree that these issues can provide food for thought—and discussion. By "covering the waterfront" at the outset, however, you have permitted each person the opportunity to respond to his own area of interest, and to more than one if he so desires.

10. *Don't Bear Down*—It is likely that a variety of responses will be forthcoming at first. An initial time for ventilation is necessary; that is, a time when each individual seeks to express his thoughts without relation to his neighbors'. Then, slowly, if you are watching for it, you will see some people starting to respond to others. Finally, there will be a body of related beginning material which you can synthesize, summarize and focus in such a way as to encourage unified discussion. This approach permits the agenda to flow easily *from the group,* and in all probability the concerns that emerge first will be the safer, less threatening, more commonly shared ones, such as health, housing and finances. This is no accident, so proceed slowly without attempting to force people into self-searching.

11. *Keep Your Goals in Mind—Help the Discussion To Ripen*—As the group leader, try always to keep your goals consciously in mind. Listen to all the factual statements about inferior housing, inadequate finances, failing health, etc., but keep directing the discussion so that

you can get at the attitudes and feelings which surround these facts. Yours is not merely a discussion group but a *mental health education* discussion group, which means that your responsibility is of a particular nature.

In one community, group members complained about inadequate finances. The leader knew that most of them were of limited means but were managing independently and had sufficient funds for clothing, food, shelter and some modest extras. After exploration, the group agreed that this was so. They were not in immediate need. What was really troubling many of them (several were unattached persons living alone) was lack of resources to attend to the details of burial—the purchase of a plot, undertaker's fees, and the like. Although this wasn't worked out in one session, the feelings of isolation, of the uncertainty surrounding their eventual demise, were channeled into some constructive solution. A group of delegates, under the aegis of the agency, which took this over as a community action project, began work with the local minister and local undertakers. The church began to take more responsibility for direct help in this area, the undertakers to explore financially cooperative ventures.

How was the group leader helpful in this situation?

a) He could have been content with the feeling of empathy the group shared on this point and permitted the discussion to burn itself out. But he went beyond this. He admitted to himself that this was a serious, very real concern of his group that would continue to plague the members, unless something practical could be done.

b) He didn't encourage the members in pipe dreams about idealistic solutions but rather found one part of the problem that lent itself to action along practical lines.

c) He had an idea about meeting this aspect of the problem and he shared it with the members, which gave them a feeling of hope and expectancy. They felt reassured at being understood.

d) He outlined a structure which would make possible the growth of the idea: a volunteer delegation which might meet with the agency director. It was a start toward control of the situation and permitted a sense of competence to replace feelings of helplessness.

e) The whole experience strengthened the group's self-esteem. Such an accomplishment can give a group the courage to try other things, to think about the power of groups, to see their agency in a new way as a force in the community.

12. *Develop a Sense of Timing*—Sessions seem to average out between an hour and an hour and a half in most groups. With this as a rough guide, try to get a sense of the right time to end the session. A session should end when the group is enthusiastic and really involved, and at a natural time of closure. Don't wait for the conversation to lag or the discussion to fall apart. Hopefully, members will be left with something to think about, wanting more and eager to return for the following session.

13. *Terminate and Summarize*—Acknowledge the fact that everyone who wanted to speak may not have had the chance. Think how frustrating it is for the long-silent member who, at last reassured, finds the session ending just as he's getting up the nerve to say something. Suggest that all members hang on to their questions—you'll try to get to them next time.

The question of summarizing the highlights is left to the leader. This technique can be helpful inasmuch as it leaves members with a sense of accomplishment and often a better understanding of the material discussed. If he has sensed the emergence of a particular area of interest, the leader might suggest they delve into it more deeply next week. Or he might simply say that the group has covered a lot of ground and it seems apparent they will have plenty to talk about next time.

The leader's approach is likely to invite the presentation of personal problems. If the first session has been filled with these, some members might conclude that this promises to be a very gloomy activity. (Why should anyone want to spend an hour just listening to other people's miseries?) The leader should make every effort to assure the group that setting forth their concerns is only the beginning. Emphasis will be on working together to do something about them.

14. *Finishing Touches*—As the meeting ends, remind everyone of

the time and place for the next session and dismiss the group. If no notes have been taken during the meeting, it would be wise to jot them down as soon as possible, while information is still fresh. Later on, a more detailed record may be written.

You might wish to carry the group discussion experience further by sharing highlights of it with agency staff who may or may not have sat in as observers. Among these colleagues, you might find it worthwhile to explain, justify and question your own actions and the group's responses, as simply or as complicatedly as the staff's sophistication will permit. (Sophistication is often greater even among volunteers than the experienced professional might think!) This sharing helps staff become conscious of possible and appropriate action they might help the members to take. For example, a prevalent fear among older people living alone is that of falling while getting in or out of the bathtub. In one community, the agency decided to get a catalogue of simple safety devices which can be attached to the tub. Thought was given as to who might pay for these, how landlords might be asked to cooperate, etc. The agency found itself involved in the problem of housing on a very simple yet meaningful level. Was it appropriate for them to do it? They decided it was, on the basis that anything which lessens physical fear contributes enormously to the general comfort and well-being of the older person.

Summary

We have tried to indicate here some of the behavior and some of the contingencies the new leader might anticipate with a new group. Working with groups, however, is a dynamic, flexible experience. Make use of those suggestions which seem natural and comfortable and improvise the rest. Eventually you will develop the style and approach that work best for you.

We have pointed out that the members of the group will probably anticipate and continue to feel a sense of enjoyment about the series. The experience should be satisfying for almost everyone—try to make it so for all! Under such conditions, a mistake in judgment should be noted and its repetition avoided. But don't worry about your errors. Everyone makes them. Whatever you have done, if you have approached your task with sincerity, goodwill and respect for the members, you'll seldom do any harm and the chances are you will have done more good than you realized.

[CHAPTER EIGHT]

Methods and Techniques of Group Discussion

Based on experience, the following methods and techniques have been found to be effective.

Advance Preparation

It is reasonable to assume that the leader will have to take a more active role at the beginning of a series than later on. He should go to the first session prepared with some facts and background material, ready to stimulate discussion with leading questions. This will help to establish him as a knowledgeable authority, will set people at ease, and will give them a broad range of reference for comments. Depending on the group, material presented could include such data as general census statistics about the aging, population shifts, immigration trends, pertinent legislation, local and national gains in health, new medical theories, housing, retirement trends and the like. In another situation it might be best to open with an explanation of the adjustments to be expected and the shifts in roles that occur in the later years of adult life. The leader need not "spill everything he knows" about the subject—his opening is primarily for the purpose of sowing seeds of thought and discussion.

Besides laying the groundwork for discussion, the leader must create an atmosphere in which group members can quickly learn to trust and respect him. They need to be reassured about the sanctity of their private thoughts, and this respect for individual privacy is implied when the leader talks in broad general terms. By opening discussion in this way, then, the leader not only reassures the skeptic, but clarifies the purpose of the meetings and establishes the tone the series will take.

Let the Group Choose Its Focus

If one starts with the premise that each group is special and different, the danger of stereotyping its members by age group or socio-economic class will be minimized. By presenting the subject to be discussed in broad and general terms the leader makes it possible for the group to respond to any one of a number of aspects. In other words, although he may have a general idea of what will concern them, he has no set outline and no predetermined notion of what they will be most anxious to talk about. He lets the agenda flow from the group, so that they may respond to subjects according to their particular needs.

Limit Your Responses

There is an old Freudian joke about one psychiatrist offering another a cigar. The recipient ponders over the hidden meaning of the gift until the giver assures him that "sometimes a cigar is just a cigar." So it often is with the verbal responses of group members. They mean what they say and nothing more. There are times, however, when material about which the members have strong feelings may be disguised behind seemingly unrelated remarks. When a group keeps hammering away at a topic, the leader might consider the subject being discussed and then ask himself, "What is it they are really trying to say? What is the concern that underlies all these illustrations?" For example, suppose a group professes great interest in medical knowledge and biological technicalities. They get involved in case illustrations, attitudes about doctors and so forth. It is possible that what this group really wants is reassurance about their own physical status and future. The key to helping them is to find a way of bringing their generalized fears and anxieties into the open, rather than supplying data better handled by a visiting expert such as a physician. The leader's contribution here might be to help the members see this and encourage them to invite a doctor to talk with them at a future session. (It goes without saying that the doctor chosen should be one with a reassuring manner and an understanding sympathy with the concerns of the elderly.)

Individual Concerns

In almost every group there will be members who have lost a job, a close friend, a brother or sister, a spouse. There may also be those with progressive and distressing physical ailments, severe financial problems or family difficulties. These concerns influence the way a person participates in a group and especially the content to which he responds. In one group a member was on leave of absence from her place of employment and had to make a decision about retiring within a period of a few months. In most discussions she participated easily, but whenever the question of work was raised her responses were fraught with anxiety and tension. At such times, her remarks became highly personalized; she tended to shut out the group and to focus on the leader as one might turn to a personal counselor or therapist.

The leader could sense the danger of the situation, but his knowledge of the individual's current problem helped him to introduce or direct discussion material to her with sensitivity and caution. After repeated and consistent generalizing about retirement had made it possible for the entire group to participate in this aspect of the discussions and to lend understanding, empathy and support to the troubled individual, she could begin to speak freely about her concern and to address her questions to her peers rather than to the leader. "What do some of the others think?" is a useful question for the leader to ask in such instances.

Adjust to the Group's Level

Having a real sense and knowledge of who his members are deters the leader from standardizing his approach—an error that can lead to its being, in some cases too intellectual, in others oversimplified and condescending.

A certain amount of pertinent information about individuals will be freely revealed by the members themselves, once they are in the group. Another source of information about individual problems is the person in charge of the over-all program. Before the group gets started and also in later conversations, the group leader might ask this person to share certain key information about the members. Such background will be helpful in shaping the leader's approach to individual members and will provide a broader basis for understanding their responses.

Each group member has had his or her share of failures and successes, of painful as well as positive experiences. His personality is conditioned by the kinds of social, cultural, educational and economic opportunities he has had all his life. The witty, sophisticated case illustration which would fit perfectly in a professional symposium might be totally inappropriate in certain groups. The members simply wouldn't understand it and the leader would have succeeded only in damaging his rapport. It is not illogical for a group to conclude that if they don't understand the leader's level of communication, he in turn does not really understand them.

Handling Threatening Material

Working with people in groups is something like getting used to bifocals—not easy, as anyone who has tried it knows. Through one lens, the leader "sees" his group as a whole; through the other he observes the individual member in close detail. He is always concerned with both. His responsibility is to provide a feasible structure for healthy group life, and to succeed at this he must discourage anything which might stand in the way. For this reason, he tries not to let any member arrive at the point of baring hidden feelings so strong and deep that their revelation might later cause him undue embarrassment or discomfort in his relationship with the others, or—conversely—might threaten, frighten or otherwise grossly upset the group.

Having initially explained the positive goals and purposes of the group, the leader has in a sense promised that this would not happen, and members have a right to expect protection from inadvertent self-revelation. The leader can provide this protection in a variety of ways.

If a member begins to get into an area of difficulty or of exclusive concern, the leader might remind him that individual consultation after the meeting is available and that "in this group we try to talk about things that involve everyone." He can directly interrupt by saying that this cannot be discussed now, or he can pick up one suitable element and redirect the discussion to the group at large. It goes without saying that kindness and respect must pervade any such comment. The member should not feel that the leader doesn't care about him, but rather that he cares enough to limit him in a situation where he may be heading for difficulties.

Limit Your Goals

We all use defense mechanisms of one type or another to deny our own shortcomings or certain aspects of life too unpleasant to accept. The ugliness of life stripped down to the bare bitter truth is a hard pill for even a saint to swallow—and few of us are saints. We are ordinary people trying to cope in the best way we know with the challenge of daily living. The elderly members of a group will bring with them patterns of adjustment developed over periods of sixty to ninety years, patterns which have permitted them to maintain their functioning. An educational discussion group is not the place to rush in and thoughtlessly or deliberately attempt to upset these patterns or to remove the personal defenses which accompany them. The carefully considered decision to do this on any level is better made by specially trained persons who are prepared to offer accompanying supportive therapy.

In one group, an 84-year-old woman, Mrs. S, proudly explained that she preferred public transportation and solitary travel to the company of friends and the comfort of their cars. While she considered her fierce independence an unquestionable asset, the group leader did not, and in fact suspected it of being a manifestation of certain weakness. He fell into the trap of trying to help this woman gain insight which might necessitate changes in behavior that was quite acceptable both to her and to the world around her. This produced very negative reactions. What happened was this: As the discussion wore on and various members gave illustrations related to the general subject of friendship, the leader remarked that sometimes it was necessary to say thank you to someone in order to enjoy that person's friendship. Mrs. S sensed that the comment was directed at her and snapped back that she often said thank you to people. The leader replied that he didn't mean the kind of thank-you spoken when someone handed you a cup of coffee, but the sort of thank-you expressed to someone in appreciation of a deed performed from a sense of concern or feeling of real responsibility. Mrs. S got redder as she replied that she felt a lot of concern for others, and she usually took responsibility and tried to be helpful. Obviously this member was hostile and angry—the leader had threatened her defenses. The next time the subject came up, the leader corrected the mistake by generalizing. He spoke very broadly about interdependency, the way people show concern, the need for people to feel that they can give as well as take, and so on. This made it possible for the entire group to become involved. It threatened no one in particular and permitted possible modification of attitudes in those persons free enough to question themselves.

Permit the Group To Lead

In spite of the most careful interpretation, it is possible for members to assume that this is a group where they will be "lectured to." When such an expectation exists the leader can be lured into doing exactly this. To avoid such a trap, the leader must constantly focus on the questions and responses of the group, handling these in such a way that the members become excited by the possibility of discovering their own thoughts and the wealth of ideas they can produce and share. The value of this experience far exceeds that which can be derived from passive listening, but members must learn this directly. They cannot unless the leader consistently does everything to make a free give-and-take possible. He should trust the group. He must not feel that unless he intervenes the conversation will come to a standstill, or that if he doesn't make a certain point, no one else will. The group members themselves will come to accept this trust and feel their share of the responsibility for keeping discussion moving.

The Passive Member

Sometimes a potential member will ask to join the group but explains that he doesn't like to talk much and would rather listen. Once in the group he might say, "I don't talk much but I'm taking it all in." Such a person is participating in his own way and should be accepted with equality and respect. The word "participate" is used deliberately because, although this member may not be active, he may be *acted upon*. He is participating to the extent that he permits himself to be part of something which may well be affecting him.

Nevertheless, since active involvement is so meaningful in these groups, it is a legitimate goal for the leader to seek for all. It may be impossible, however, for all members to achieve this goal or to achieve it in equal degree. There are many subtle shades of involvement which indicate that the member is responding, or that he wants to move on to another level. An observant leader may see a member who has been sitting sideways and slouching for several sessions suddenly turn full face toward the other members. His facial expression may change to one of alertness, or he may begin to reveal his interest by stopping more often to comment after the session ends. In one group, a woman sat until the twelfth session and said nothing. Suddenly she began to speak up and made several contributions. She explained afterwards that we had started talking about children and since she was interested in them, she felt she had something she wanted to say. Although it is likely that her interest had been previously aroused, this member needed three months of support, acceptance and testing before she was able to speak. If she had been treated as a lost cause or if the leader had pressured her, this could not have happened.

Sometimes a member may dare to open up only in the "safety" of the last session. But even members who end a series as silently as they began it may well have demonstrated by virtue of their regular attendance that the experience had meaning for them. These people also play a significant role in the total group experience by helping others to be more accepting of different types of participation and to develop mutual respect and trust despite such differences.

Strengths within
the Group

As groups become more cohesive, they gain a sense of their own power. They become excited by the decisions they are able to make, the thoughts they are able to provoke. To experience real sharing and honest communication is highly satisfying. Once this satisfaction has been experienced, the group will use itself to sanction or reject any individual behavior which affects these rewards. They may limit members who "hog the floor," become too personal, or try repeatedly to discuss ideas or experiences out of range of common sharing. On the positive side, they may also offer support to the meek and timid or encouragement to the depressed.

Pressure from one's peers often makes limitations palatable, because the basic concept assures each member of the same right. Others may be limiting him today, but he can limit someone else tomorrow. We encourage this form of self-government out of respect for the capacity of the group members. The leader is of course justified in intervening under certain conditions—when, for example, an individual is being chastised to the point at which his future freedom of expression or his relationships are endangered, or where the group is doing nothing to stop a situation that is clearly headed for difficulties. Suppose that an individual seems unaware of the hostility which—for whatever reason —he provokes in others; he may be greeted at future meetings with facial expressions of scorn and annoyance or even with verbal brickbats. ("Do we have to listen to him again!") Allowing such a member free rein alienates him from the group and does not really give him the help he is seeking. The experience may be so unrewarding that he does not return. On the other hand, once the leader recognizes the situation he can limit the member who gets out of bounds by intervening and generalizing his comments. This will make him feel he has contributed something important and permits the group to see that he can make a worthwhile contribution. It prevents them from using him as a scapegoat and prevents him from feeling that he and his ideas are unwanted.

Help the Group To Focus

During a discussion, the group may talk of a wide variety of things. From time to time, the leader can be helpful by pulling together assorted ideas and information, so that the discussion becomes more sharply focused and thoughts are directed toward specifics. He may summarize what the group has said and add information of his own. This technique may be used at the beginning of a meeting in order to pick up a previous discussion, or intermittently during the meeting, or at the conclusion. There are no hard-and-fast rules about the use of this technique; it is a helpful tool to use when appropriate.

Recording

While the meeting is under way, the leader may see so many important things happening to various members that he will wonder if he can recollect them all for recording. As he becomes more experienced, however, the question of what to record is less troublesome because he soon learns what material is useful. The very experience of recording over and over again makes this process of selection progressively easier. The question arises, then, what kind of notes should the leader take and when should he take them?

Note-taking at the conclusion of a session will be easier for some leaders and is perfectly acceptable. Many leaders have found that certain sentences, phrases, or a name and a key word next to it have been sufficient to elicit detailed recall, assuming the leader writes up his record within a reasonable period after the meeting. It is also possible to make such notes while a meeting is in process. Provided a simple explanation is given, it usually does not disturb the group. Sometimes when the leader is reviewing or summarizing, the group may show amazement that he remembers so much. It is appropriate at such times to mention that notes were helpful. In other words, note-taking can be done easily and inconspicuously and the group can be helped to understand at least one of its purposes. Accordingly, when properly handled, note-taking during meetings need not be destructive to the relationship between the leader and the group.

Picking Up the Threads

Since the leader is basically responsible for the structure of the meeting, it is natural that he give some thought to what will happen the next time the group meets. How will they begin and what will he say?

Review notes and record material may suggest the group's desire to pick up at some particular point. But the leader may be misled. The impact of the sessions will also be felt by the members, and their recollections may lead them into a whole new area of thought or cause them to think about old material in a new way. Thus, while it is helpful and appropriate for the leader to open a session with a brief summary, highlighting particular unexplored areas, his principal responsibility is to handle those matters the group feels are important. He must be most sensitive to their responses and willing to shelve his own ideas. Chances are that his professional estimate of appropriate points for discussion are accurate. If so, they will come up again. By waiting and controlling any impulse to manipulate the discussion according to his own wishes, the leader demonstrates his sincere belief in the group's right to proceed at its own pace.

CHAPTER NINE

What Factors Affect the Group Experience?

People do not function in a vacuum. Whether they are alone or in groups many factors affect their behavior and what they gain from group experience. These factors can include not only their own individual life experiences, but such things as the kind of group they are in, its management, how it is represented to outsiders, and many more. Accordingly, the group leader should concern himself with those factors that can significantly affect the groups he works with. These most often fall into the following categories.

External Factors

SIZE OF THE GROUP. When a discussion group is too small (less than 7 or 8 persons, usually) the leader faces a special kind of risk. He may find himself playing a very active role trying to keep the participants from becoming too personal, or he may be drawn into talking too much in order to keep things moving. The intimacy fostered by having so few persons in the group may cause the members to view the leader as one of them—to assimilate him, so to speak. On the other hand, a group that is too large (more than 20 to 25) can be frustrating to members who do not get a chance to speak and thus may foster intolerance toward those who do. Sometimes members feel lost and uninvolved and begin to drop out. If they remain, the group is likely to be overweighted by passive participants, with discussion and activity dominated by the livelier few.

The numbers cited here are of course approximations. They will vary with leader and setting. They are merely intended to serve as guides in avoiding the problems in group functioning mentioned above.

GROUP COMPOSITION.   It is possible to experience a good measure of success by hit-or-miss group enrollment. There are reasons, however, why enrollment is best worked out jointly with a staff person who has some knowledge of the organization's over-all membership. When such a person understands how group composition can affect achievement of goals, it may be possible to balance the discussion group to some extent. People's approaches to discussion are seldom uniform. Differences occur and these can be healthy and helpful. In a well-mixed group, the secure member can offer support to the timid; the intellectually sophisticated can introduce unusual thoughts and deepen the general level of exploration.

Churchwomen's leagues, men's lodges and PTAs are examples of groups which include many different personalities. They could not function in a healthy way if, for example, every churchwoman detested the choirmaster, every man in the lodge thought the program was so good there was no need ever to improve it, or every member of the PTA was so disheartened by the school's inadequacies that he felt any effort at betterment would be futile. While these examples are extreme, they illustrate the point that differences in personality and attitude among members help to promote a realistic balance of thinking and opinion.

It is especially important to avoid group composition which includes all the problem cases in the agency—all the depressed and withdrawn, all the active fault-finders, or even all the positive, well-adjusted individuals—unless the leader consciously wants to experiment with such a grouping and has the specialized skill or personnel that may be required. Such special groups can be misinterpreted in the agency-community. "All the sick ones belong," it might be said, or "all the smart ones," or "all the big shots." Such labeling can be unfortunate.

So the leader should seek balance but not be too selective. The large majority of people can participate and benefit from mental health education groups; whenever possible all interested persons should have this opportunity. In a well-mixed, varied group, people tend to help and reinforce each other toward common goals.

SHIFTS IN ATTENDANCE.   Attendance statistics are easy to keep. They should be kept—and analyzed. Variations may indicate members' adverse reactions to uninteresting, threatening or inappropriate subject matter that must be reckoned with. On the other hand, they may simply reflect certain reality factors, such as pressure of holidays, severe weather conditions, a mild epidemic, or competing activities over which the leader has little control. The leader should be aware of how many come and go irregularly; who does not return; whether any of these have become ill or have died. Some of these factors may afford the group subjects to discuss. Instances of sickness and death are particularly important. They may present an opportunity for shared compassion or farewell, and a reaffirmation of the meaning of life as well as acceptance of death. If a certain member who has come regularly does not return after a specific discussion in which he or she was involved, the absence should be followed up by staff in order to find out whether the discussion raised problems on which further help or clarification is needed.

PHYSICAL SETTING.   Who among us hasn't seen a good show in a hot, airless theater and realized afterwards that he didn't really enjoy it because of the physical surroundings? Creature comforts are important to group members. Certain conditions can be distracting and can make it difficult to concentrate on subject matter. A room may be too hot or too cold, too large or too small.

When one group met in a spacious but drafty basement room, the members preferred to huddle together in a corner. This caused crowding, presented difficulties for latecomers and prevented a more relaxed and open seating arrangement.

Noise due to nearby activities, the well-intentioned volunteer preparing refreshments at the back of the room, or people interrupting a session with phone messages are all equally disconcerting. Groups which demand an emotional investment are particularly sensitive to this sort of distraction. Unlike groups which are activity-centered, such as a metalwork class, discussion groups must have a relatively protected meeting place.

A circle, semicircle or large table suitable for grouping will help create a setting wherein feelings of informality and unity may more easily develop. Most important, these arrangements do not physically set the leader apart from the group. Although it is not impossible to have a good group experience in a room set up like a classroom or auditorium, this kind of arrangement has distinct disadvantages. People cannot see the faces of the other participants. They are likely to become overinvolved with the leader at the front of the room, who stands out like a lecturer or guest speaker. The very nature of a classroom setting may unintentionally suggest that the responsibility for achieving participation is solely the leader's or that he is there to "tell" the group rather than to help them interact and share.

Psychological and Structural Factors

The cooperation and understanding of everyone in the larger organization who is related to the group membership are very important. Staff might give token acceptance to a series but not want to assume the further responsibilities that arise from it. Or they might declare their "whole-hearted support" and then unconsciously or deliberately withhold their involvement because of work pressures or lack of interest in the project. They may feel the program was forced on them and is merely to be tolerated rather than supported. To avoid such situations insofar as possible, the staff should have a chance to discuss feelings about mental health education groups and to express any doubts or misgivings they may have—in advance. They are the ones logically responsible for motivating initial interest in group membership, and hopefully they will carry on and further develop the benefits gained from the group discussions.

Beyond this, conviction is needed on the part of staff, to handle the reactions of group members—and the reactions of others in the larger organizations as well—once the program gets off the ground. (For example: "What do they mean, *mental health group*? Is that a group for nuts?") Even if the discussion leader is a regular staff member, he needs staff cooperation, since it is unlikely that all questions or comments about the group will come directly to him.

In most settings, mental health education will be a new program that must pass the test of acceptance. The job has to be shared by everyone. All staff members have to put their weight behind it in order for it to succeed.

In the project on which this report is based, the discussion leader has been an outsider coming into a center only to lead the discussion group. In many cases the center staff was working against difficulties that created real hardships—lack of adequate personnel, limited budget, etc. Coming into this kind of difficult, long-term situation, a leader may occasionally feel that a kind of subtle sabotage is at work. And he may be right. Consider the situation from the permanent staff's point of view. The leader comes in fresh. He or she has a special aura, even glamour, for the group members. He is a new face. He is not taken for granted as they so often are. It would be unrealistic to expect the often-discouraged, harassed and tired staff to remain free of negative or rivalrous feelings. Therefore, it is not unusual to find permanent staff unconsciously undermining such a program.

The degree to which this may occur depends in part on how the decision to have a mental health discussion group was arrived at. Was it a decision based on careful discussion among the staff as a whole or was it an edict "handed down from on high"? Ideally, this kind of project should be interpreted and presented for consideration to all who work directly with the members, so that questions and doubts can be openly raised, fully discussed and—hopefully—answered. Otherwise, status problems emerge. The volunteer worker may feel excluded; the untrained staff member may feel inferior or resentful. Unless these feelings can be handled openly and directly, there may be ambivalence and even hostility toward the program.

Quality of Service and
Philosophy of the Host Agency

We know that during the life of a series there are valuable goals to be achieved entirely within the meetings. Discussions can produce such phenomena as catharsis or ventilation, emotional support, ego development and beginning insights. Sometimes, however, the goals of improving every member's self-image, confidence and security can best be achieved by action taken outside the discussion group. For example, concern about isolation of the elderly might lead to helping the group members become meaningfully involved with another group in an entirely different age range. Or the problem of solitary eating might stimulate action to institute a lunch program, in turn necessitating communication with a policy-making board. This could in time lead to a valuable development in the organization's program and in the members' sense of worthwhile accomplishment. Or it could lead to real disappointment. If the agency views itself primarily as a recreational or educational service, it may feel it beyond its scope to foster an extended social life for group members or to assume responsibility for a more social lunch program. The need and desire for such services may be entirely valid but the leader must understand the limitations as well as the opportunities of the setting. If he does not, he is in danger of directing the group toward frustration in the form of unattainable goals or even unresolved conflict with the rest of the agency.

Judged by professional standards, one practical measure of an agency's quality is the amount of trained staff available to individualize services. While volunteers bring their own special qualities to the agency, it is not fair to expect the same caliber of performance from. them as from qualified professionals.

Since skilled and experienced staff are in short supply generally, it is realistic to assume that the professionally trained leader will often find himself in settings where philosophy and standards seem to him limited, ineffectual or even destructive. He should bear in mind that primarily the agency has asked him to do a specific job, not to evaluate the total program. If he keeps this focus, some disappointment will be avoided, not to mention the dangerous feeling that the staff "isn't worth bothering with." He must proceed from the premise that the most limited person—staff member or client—can broaden his horizon; and, likewise, that the total agency can be improved through the work of his own group. When the leader undertakes his task with this accepting attitude, the staff will not be threatened by his rapport with his group, or by his special knowledge and skill. They will see him and the experience as adding another dimension to the existing program and possibly stimulating and enhancing their own work.

Even in the best and most congenial settings, the discussion leader who is brought in as an "expert" should recognize that he usually has special skill and experience not shared by his colleagues. The intensity of sharing with the staff will vary from setting to setting, but the need will always be there. Should the leader foolishly decide to hide within the sanctum of his specialty, concerned only with himself and his group, he will soon find his ivory tower crumbling. He will have been responsible for ignoring one of the basic factors already mentioned as vital to the life of the discussion group.

If the group members feel that the staff—whatever their degree of training—see them as thoughtful, mature people capable of learning and eager to extend their potential, then they also will develop a special approach and greater investment in their discussion group. This reaction is fostered when the members are treated with dignity and concern by all staff, in all phases of agency program.

The Local Social Climate

Picture the impact of change upon the older person who has lived in one neighborhood for thirty years. He has known his old neighbors for a long time. If he didn't like them all, at least he was used to them, more or less. The rapid, bewildering changes and growth going on in most cities today can affect him directly and, too often, adversely.

When buildings are old, rents are cheaper; so new neighbors, usually of limited means, begin to arrive. They may have infants who scream at night and school-age children who make noise and seem disrespectful. They are often of different racial and ethnic backgrounds.

The older resident suddenly finds himself, either newly or again, part of a minority group. Many of his old neighbors have moved away and so, usually, have his own children. He knows hardly anyone in his building; even the storekeepers have changed. He feels strange and may be uncomfortable about going out after dark. He hears stories— whether factual or exaggerated, the emotional impact is similar—of muggings, thefts, gang fights and other dangers of being out alone at night.

A group leader asking the members to share their concerns and attitudes about their daily life can expect the expression of hostility, resentment, anxiety, fear and even prejudice. Such topics as retirement, family relations, health or second marriages may all seem insignificant compared with their bewilderment and anxiety about "the neighborhood situation."

This in itself can be a fruitful subject for discussion, as a result of which group members can begin to come to terms with the situation, separate real from imagined problems, and sometimes even "do something about it." Under such conditions, however, it may be some time before the group can begin to think about other issues. They need first an opportunity to air their feelings about immediate and pressing environmental problems. Now contrast such a group with one in middle-class suburbia, or perhaps in a special "retirement community." The social climate is certainly different. Members have nice stores, compatible neighbors and good physical facilities. They may have left the old neighborhood to live with children and grandchildren. Yet they are quite likely to have their own immediate concerns, concentrated about such problems as role, isolation, status, family relations and the rearing of their grandchildren.

Each group will have its own individual character, derived from the common major concerns of its members. Just as immediate externals affect the behavior of members in the group, so does social climate affect the kinds of subjects they discuss and their approach to a subject.

To sum up, there are many factors which affect the group experience. Some of the leaders cannot control at all or can influence their groups only in a limited way. Other groups can be contained at least, through the leader's sensitivity and awareness. We have tried to emphasize here the important role of all staff within a sponsoring agency, and the necessity for the group leader and the staff to establish good communication and cooperation. We have encouraged leader recognition of the importance of the social climate in which the group member lives, stressing that experiences from group to group will vary accordingly. We have also acknowledged that the standards of service and philosophy of the agency affect the content of group discussion and the use of that content. We have tried to say there is no such thing as purity of method in this type of work with human beings. Understanding this frees the leader of illusions based on unrealistic misapplication of theory and helps him face the reality with which he must deal.

CHAPTER TEN

Extracts from the Records of Actual Discussions

The following are extracts taken from records of mental health education group discussions with the aging.

They are presented here to show the highlights of what actually transpired from the beginning to the end in typical sessions. How did the leader get started and what did he try to do? How did the members respond? How did the worker know goals were being reached?

It is hoped that these extracts from process recordings will answer some of these questions and, when considered in context with what has been mentioned before, will round out the picture of the purpose, nature and potential of this kind of work.

The First Session of a Ten-Session Series

Note: This record attempts to show one way of approaching a group at the first session. We can observe: (a) members' initial confusion about the group; (b) some effects of the lack of a private room for the meeting; (c) the role of the club worker; (d) the place of "fringe" group members; (e) the use of historical and sociological material; (f) the jumping from one topic to another and (g) the concluding amazement at having shared so much at the first session. What is perhaps most evident, however, is the involvement the members showed once the session got under way and their willingness to participate once the tone for communication had been set. In the end, we see the group leader take major responsibility for suggesting the following week's topic, aware that some time may pass before members can do this for themselves, and not considering in any way that this devalued the experience.

When I entered the club there were about 25 people seated in different parts of the main meeting room, with about 12 of them at a long table. Most of the people present at my general introductory session the week before were here again this week. I had previously explained the purpose of the discussion series and invited all those interested to return.

When I sat down, Mrs. M, a member, was off to my right. She told me that she expected there would be trouble, since many people came anticipating a bingo game today and that it really wasn't right for me to be there on a Wednesday. I motioned to Miss H, the staff worker, and asked her whether she thought any explanation to the people around the room was necessary? Rather sternly, she told Mrs. M that she plans the program, that the bingo game was not going on today or any other Wednesday at this time, and that this had been all settled with the members previously. (After the meeting was over I discovered that Mrs. M had had the same argument with Miss H prior to my coming and obviously was not quite satisfied with the outcome.) Miss H suggested that I get started, for fear that some people might begin to drift into the other room.

I began the same way I had the week before, by introducing myself as a social worker. I explained that my agency was interested in seeing that all people had a better life. I told them that in the past the agency had had requests for speakers, lecturers and films concerning certain aspects of aging. We had found, when we actually sent someone to various Golden Age Clubs, that at the end of a session there were often more questions that people wanted to raise or more things they wished to say. We had concluded from this that people wanted to speak and be heard and also that we didn't really know as much as we might about people who were getting older in our city. It was important to know as much as we possibly could, because it might affect the nature of our help and we might then be able to help them more. We felt the best way to find out would be to go directly to the people and that's why I had to come and speak with them.

I gave a very brief but concentrated account of some of the sociological changes that have taken place in the United States over the last fifty or sixty years. I reminded them of the old prints that we are all familiar with, showing the traditional farmhouse kitchen with the grandmother, the grandfather, the grandchildren, the sons and daughters, very busy at work, sharing activities under one common roof. Now this is more or less a thing of the past—people don't usually live in three-generation households any more. Our cities have grown; new job opportunities have become available; sons and daughters have found it opportune to move to other cities, sometimes to other states, and consequently we now have many older people living alone who never had to face this situation before. Not only do we have more people in this situation, but we have in our total population more people than ever before over the age of 60. I reiterated that we really don't know as much as we might about the needs and concerns of these people. Maybe they weren't the same as the early settlers who went to California with mining pans or set out for the West in covered wagons, but in a sense they were living in times just as challenging and even more difficult. We hoped we could learn from them and that we could tell others what we learned. Perhaps they could even learn from each other, too, by getting a new slant on their own approaches after really understanding the ways in which a neighbor had chosen to meet his concerns. Could we begin by mentioning what those concerns might be?

There was an awkward moment of silence, but Mrs. R soon spoke up and said that one of the concerns she faced was poor health and the fact that it slows you down; you can't do what you used to do anymore. Mrs. G (the woman who had mentioned to me the week before that she had sent for a booklet and found it helpful) said that even when your health slows you down you still had to keep active, that people need people and this was really the important thing. She said that even though this was so, she didn't particularly think that living together with other people was such a good idea, and felt it important to maintain your independence. She didn't want to be thought of as a baby-sitter and nothing else. Mrs. M responded by observing that people say "Live alone and like it" and some of us live alone, but we don't like it.

Mr. M commented that economic changes had created a housing problem in our society and even if these things were understood, what were we going to do about it? From this point on, the conversation focused on housing. Mrs. M said that she would rather go into a nursing home than have to live with her children, and there was a great deal of comment about children. Mrs. M's daughter had reflected on some of her mother's reported activities (such as a masquerade at the club) by saying that "everybody over there must be in his second childhood." The mother said she felt this remark was made without understanding and showed a certain lack of respect. "True, we don't always make the best companions for one another but at least many times we understand each other better than the young people do. Mrs. S, a woman in her eighties who was seated on the fringe of the group, knitting, commented that her daughter alters her dresses for her so that they are, to her way of thinking, always too short and too tight. She feels her daughter attempts to make her look younger, which is inappropriate and unbecoming.

Mr. M went back to the question of housing and said that he'd been reading that people all over the world, even in places as far away as Thailand, are experiencing some of the same problems as we. This gave me an opportunity again to remind them that once you get into an urban culture you begin to have certain problems and this is true no matter what part of the world people inhabit. (In a sense, this observation helped them identify with troubled people much beyond their own private circle.)

Miss G, with a great deal of passion and anger, reflected upon her experiences in looking for housing. She felt there was a general attitude that as a single person you could shift for yourself and live independently anywhere, that adequate public housing was not necessarily one of your needs. She said that if anybody deserves a decent place to live, single people do; they deserve it and need it very much. She said she didn't consider this a situation where you can just shift for yourself. There followed a long discussion about the terribly high rents in the neighborhood and the members' inability to meet them, as well as about the dearth of housing for the middle-income person. Mrs. M said that all these apartment houses going up all over destroy the feeling of neighborhood and neighborliness. However, she added, part of this feeling also depends upon the individual person and how much of an investment he wants to make in meeting his neighbors. Mr. M described some housing plans for the elderly used in cities such as Dallas, Texas, where they have small bungalows with four or five occupants. He said this would be one way of combatting the feeling of living in a "cold brick prison." He wondered why our city planners were so unimaginative. The other people in the group reminded him of the lack of space and the unavailability of land in our city, to which he replied there seemed to be plenty of land available for parking lots. He turned around and asked me what I thought about that. I agreed, generally, and said that the problems of the city are very hard to understand if you look at them separately, that each is part of an intricate whole made up of many problems, interwoven and interrelated. Many people have moved outside the city and helped lessen the total congestion but they still commute to work here; this accentuates the need for parking lots. Neither problem could be treated as bigger than the other; all of them added up to a bundle of complexities surrounding city life.

I took this opportunity to try to offer some perspective about what was happening in the field of public housing. Mrs. M had said earlier that families, especially those with children, didn't find adequate housing any more easily than older people; this was a problem for everyone. I reminded them that they were not alone in this problem and I recognized that they were primarily interested in themselves, not in the older population ten years from now. However, I added, if we did not look at this problem in perspective, we might feel very gloomy. Originally, I pointed out, five per cent of public housing was given over specifically for older-adult apartments, then it went up to seven per cent and now it is up to about 25 per cent. Furthermore, public housing staffs who plan space for people over 60 have been working recently with social agencies, community centers, church groups—wherever they can—to get organized expressions from older people of the architectural and social needs to be met in building. I told them of a professional friend who five years ago had worked with a group similar to theirs and who felt that their writing a letter to the Governor making recommendations for public housing was a rather exciting accomplishment. This was only five years ago and now, instead of just writing letters and dropping them into an impersonal mailbox, we get a chance to serve on committees and meet with members of the City Planning Commission and other local planning groups. They responded to this by telling me that someone had come from the Housing Authority to ask them what kind of recreation facilities they wanted. Mrs. M said: "We told them everything under the sun, so who knows what we'll get!" They all laughed about someone's request for a boccie court. I concluded by saying that we didn't have all the answers now and we don't have enough good housing to go around, but we have more of both than we used to have. In another five years, we'll have still more. Perhaps part of what we could share with one another would contribute to some of the answers. What, for example, did they think about age-segregated housing?

Soon after raising the question, I realized we had been talking for approximately an hour and twenty minutes and I suggested that perhaps it was time for us to conclude our opening session. I said we had touched on many, many things today and maybe we ought to refresh them in our minds. Maybe then we could think about a place to start the discussion next week. I reviewed many of the areas touched on—housing, independent living, attitudes of younger people, the growth of our cities, living longer with fewer satisfactions, health needs, loneliness, and so on. It was very difficult for them to select from this group; and somewhat overwhelmed by all they had said, they seemed to be unable to take this step. I suggested, and they agreed, that we would start with the question Mrs. P had raised earlier, that of health. I selected this subject because I felt it was of major concern to all of them and would not seem so emotionally difficult to discuss as might, for example, attitudes of young people, loneliness, or living longer without satisfactions. They could return expecting the familiar, something they were used to talking about.

(In my own mind, I thought of focusing on *attitudes* connected with specific health problems which might be raised, since I was not qualified to answer clinical health questions. Around diet, for example, I might direct discussion toward the problem of having to eat alone and its effect upon adequate food preparation and appetite. Around clinic visits and doctors, I might get into the question of the doctor as someone who cares and makes one feel important, or the socialization possible in clinic waiting rooms.)

As the session concluded, Mr. M chuckled and said he had thought I would be doing something quite different from what I had. He guessed he confused mental health with physical health. He revealed that he believed I had come today to begin leading a calisthenics group! Members and I responded with a good deal of laughter. The meeting ended informally with members exchanging anecdotes about experiences and physical exercises.

The Ninth Session of a Ten-Session Series

Note: This record attempts to show how the leader made use of memories and recall in order to emphasize the vastness and value of past experiences, and their effect upon members' present and future life.

The content for today's meeting was related to memories of the past and the effect of changes on the members at this time. All present were American-born. Perhaps three were born New Yorkers; five others came from Virginia, Missouri, Oklahoma and Chicago, Illinois. Early childhood memories were plentiful in their comments, by contrast with immigrant groups, where emphasis was usually on life after arrival in the United States.

The members talked about the first automobiles, the first nickelodeons, the hansom cabs with drivers in high hats and passengers coming from the docks past 25th Street. They spoke of high-stoop brownstones and houses with wine cellars. They mentioned strolling musicians, old German bands and organ-grinders; Paddy's Market on the West Side in the forties, and shopping with a "growler," a tin milk container. They mentioned the water jugs and basins used before indoor plumbing; Prohibition; the Grand Opera House with its beautiful carved wooden doors, and theatrical stars like Lily Langtry. Those who grew up outside New York remembered

Indians and—in one case—being introduced to Buffalo Bill. They recalled tents set up on street corners for recruitment during the Spanish-American War, and one man remembered camping grounds in Missouri where soldiers of this war had stayed. They remembered when Bryan was nominated; described the collection of drinking water in rain barrels. They talked of the first victrola spool record; flatirons, then gas irons, and fluting machines to match the fancy, ruffled fashions of the day; the advent of electric irons and vacuum cleaners. They had seen movies go from the five-cent silent films to the talkies. They thought that people were friendlier and different in the old days; they were closer and you knew your neighbors. You weren't afraid to leave your doors open. They talked of the new foods available today, how easy they are to prepare and how handy that you can freeze them. They admitted that in general people have many more conveniences and more leisure now. But nowadays people seem to look outside for the entertainment they once made with a family group at home. They spoke of coal bins outside of grocery stores; the transition from gas to electricity for lighting; the disappearance of the lamplighter, the corncob stove, and the foot warmers you used to take to bed with you. Miss A said, "When it's cold now, you just knock on the steam pipe."

They thought that when they were younger, children had lots more responsibility than they have now. They watched the introduction of fire departments, labor unions and changes in pay scales. They spoke of social changes, "big social changes" (and they used those words) like greater attempts to achieve equal rights for all, and more opportunities for education. They noted the increase in the number of jobs requiring special knowledge and how it was harder and harder for unskilled laborers to find jobs because of technological changes. They were aware of the programs of retraining for certain jobs, and they mentioned the institution of Social Security and the possibility of a new medical care program. Miss G said she felt life was becoming more and more difficult, and that was one of the reasons we had more mental cases now than we ever had before.

They said they felt that elderly people were much more aware, involved and concerned in the world outside their families than they ever had been before.

In trying to focus this material, I took the comment that Mr. M had made: "One of the things I know is, that you can't ever go back to the place where you've come from; things are all changed." Very sadly, he had told about looking for the candy store he used to go to as a boy. It wasn't there any more; other familiar landmarks had also disappeared from the scene. He added that he guessed he'd changed too. We all agreed that you can't actually go back. Knowing that, what was the alternative? You could either stand still, stagnate, and in a sense die, or you could move forward. I said I felt they were making the choice; they were moving forward by admitting and demonstrating that they were very much interested in other people as well as themselves and in the world around them.

Miss G had in great detail described her ancestors as Scottish Highlanders who pioneered in covered wagons to Iowa. Their log cabin was one of the first built by settlers in that State. I observed that perhaps they had never considered themselves as pioneers in the same sense; yet if they looked back over the myriad changes that they had lived through without having a pattern to follow, they would see that they too could be considered a special kind of pioneer.

Mr. Asa C had told the group he had been to a meeting in Washington on the question of special services for older adults. I said some day a grandnephew of his might talk about his great-uncle Asa as one of the people who made such-and-such kind of legislation possible by demonstrating an interest and acting in concert with others to see that it was passed. Mr. C laughed and said perhaps he could think of himself as a pioneer. Miss G said that she too could qualify, since by chairing a committee she had been instrumental in helping the union get started in her shop. Little by little, members around the room began to tell ways in which they had pioneered.

Comment: I think the use of recall helped the members to realize all that they had lived through, and the necessity and their willingness to adapt to change. It emphasized how much they had participated in life—and contributed to it. While there was momentary sadness about not being able to go back, either to change what is past or to eliminate past changes, there was by the end of the discussion much more focus on the strengths they were still using and might continue to use in the future.

For those who may wish to pursue further the subject of recall, a helpful article may be found in a reprint from *Psychiatry: Journal for the Study of Interpersonal Processes* (Vol. 26, No. 1, Feb. 1963), "The Life Review: An Interpretation of Reminiscence in the Aged," by Robert N. Butler.

The Fifth Session of an Eleven-Session Series, with a Staff Observer Present

Note: On reading this record, it is hard to believe that this group had the most difficult time of any in getting started. As the leader, I felt throughout the first four meetings that, despite a variety of approaches, I was not really reaching the members, nor were they really sharing with each other. At the fifth session a feeling of openness and cohesion suddenly emerged, only to support again the dictum that one must be patient and wait for that indefinable time when members show signs of really functioning as a group. The record attempts to show how the leader tried to elicit and explore feelings related to growing older, to recognize problems which were difficult to cope with, and to emphasize positive opportunities for hope and growth. It also shows the increasing interest of the staff observer and the attempt of the leader to involve her. Note that the leader was helped by the observer as well when she offered her support and recognition.

Mrs. H, the staff observer, was present today after a week's absence. Several new people had come to the group today along with Mrs. H, and I briefly explained the purpose of our sessions, summarizing the previous week's material. Last week's session had ended with a question open for further exploration: What are the best periods in one's life? The group continued to discuss them. Those mentioned were:

a) *Childhood*—The feelings presented were those that expressed freedom from worry, the joy of receiving gifts at holiday time, and the conclusion that there was a tremendous feeling of being loved and protected.

b) *The "earning years"*—The feelings involved were those of accomplishment—being busy, saving money—and of independence and helpfulness to others.

c) *Courtship*—This was recalled as a time completely free of worries.

d) *Early married life*—Seen as a time when one had everything one wanted.

e) *Waiting for one's children to be born*—Seen as a period of great expectation and anticipation.

As is clear from the listing, these periods were greatly romanticized, with the realities and hardships eliminated. However, the group did not seem to feel that they were seeing them in an idealized way. Certainly by comparison with what they had now these periods were full and happy.

I took up the question of the time when one was gainfully employed and asked them to examine individually the feelings they had mentioned. I asked them whether, with the exception of being able to save money, they did not have the opportunity at present to be involved in the same ways they had been involved before. Could they not, for example, be busy now? Wasn't it possible to feel a sense of independence even within the confines of a very small and limited budget, and could they not still experience the satisfaction of helping others? What evolved was that it was at present possible to continue with these things, but that physical limitations served as a severe handicap. We went into a lengthy discussion of the fact that one's body begins aging as soon as it has matured and, if we were to be honest, all along the path of life everybody has some kind of ache or pain that he must live with. Although handicaps may become more severe as one ages, it was obvious that none of the members was actually incapacitated. All could get around, be out among people, come to the club. Mrs. M said that though this was true, she, for example, has been forbidden by her doctor to read or to paint, two things she enjoys tremendously. She uses much of her time knitting because her eyes need not be involved. I asked Mrs. M to try and remember how old she was when she began to paint, knowing that she was well along when she started. She admitted she was 80 and now she was 84. If one door could open at the age of 80 and possibly be closed again at the age of 84, might it not be possible, I asked, for another door to open at 85? Mrs. M shook her head and said she did not think so. I asked her if she was content that she had tried and used all her capacities? She said no, she had to admit that she was not. Perhaps, she allowed, she could become involved in new and different things which she had not thought about, although she didn't have much faith in the possibility.

(At the conclusion of the series, Mrs. M had a secure place as a natural leader of the discussion group. One year later, the permanent club leader reported that this drive carried over into her general participation, and that she had become a forceful and effective leader in center affairs, a role she had not previously assumed.)

I did not feel that it was honest to pursue this point much further with the members, because I realized that physical limitations were very real and quite serious for all of them. As mentioned, all are able to get about; yet all have the question continuously hanging over their heads, when will their ever-increasing debilitation reach such a point that they become dependent? Many group members are quite feeble. This is a fact that does not lend itself to discussion, nor is it helpful to dwell upon it. In other words, we recognized and admitted that this limitation existed and tried to focus on what they could do within their present narrow range.

I pointed out that in summarizing the different periods of life in which each of them had felt satisfactions, it seemed to me a common element appeared—that is, the enjoyment of experiences with other people. I asked them to examine this element and to decide whether they thought opportunities still existed for them to enjoy things with others. Did they agree that this was really a way to gain satisfaction and pleasure?

A controversy then sprang up around this question of relationships with other people. The majority said that they needed people, they were used to people, and they sought them out. There was a minority, however, who said that people were all right but that, actually, one had to depend on oneself. We had talked a little bit about the elements we were seeing in our relationships with other persons when Mrs. W (our group renegade) posed another question. She wondered if it might not be true that the more we learned to depend on others, the less we were able to remain alone and depend upon ourselves? We decided to hold over this question to open discussion the following week, and the meeting formally ended here.

Comment: After the discussion, I asked Mrs. H, the staff worker, if she had noticed any difference in the group this week. She said she was rather surprised at the content and the depth of involvement. She felt the group had moved along considerably. I said I had felt the same thing and was glad to have her support my impression. We agreed that these people's discussions have a philosophical bent which is not always so obviously present with other groups. There was a time this week, for example, when we talked about "mellowing" during old age and questioned whether age in itself helps to bring this about, or whether a person has to contribute directly. There were those who admitted that they got sassier as they got older, as if to say they didn't give a darn anymore what others thought. Now they had the freedom to act as they had really wanted to act during their adult life.

CHAPTER ELEVEN

Aids to Group Discussion

Usefulness of Special Materials

Mental health education programs have for many years been greatly enriched by visual aid materials, especially plays and films dealing with such topics as normal child development, courtship and marriage, adjustment to the later years, and information about the neuroses and psychoses. There are plays and films that deal with almost every aspect of family life and with the psychological aspects of growth, personality and human relationships.

While these materials have been useful as a source of information, their main contribution has been to offer a framework for group discussion and participation. However, because they deal with complex and sensitive subjects such materials can be used improperly, and mishandling can lead more to confusion than enlightenment. Really serious misinterpretation can produce marked anxiety or anger. Years of experience have shown that the best use of visual aids is to provide audiences with some basic information and to serve as a springboard for group discussion led by a trained, experienced leader—someone, that is, with sound professional background in the subject matter to be discussed, as well as experience and training in work with discussion groups.

Many persons who might be shy and inarticulate under other conditions are able to express their ideas and tell of their own experiences after sharing a dramatized experience. The impact of such a presentation offers an added dimension to the subject discussed. There is often an immediate identification and empathy with the characters portrayed which members of the group can then relate to the ideas developed, through meaningful personal reactions.

By and large, these aids to education have been used for large meetings—the many one-night stands that are held in every community. There is no question that they do stimulate group discussion which might otherwise be extremely difficult to develop in a large audience. However, they can also play a part in programming for smaller groups.

This is especially true in working with older people, who are sometimes less able to express their feelings in words or communicate with others through discussion. A concrete, dramatic experience may be needed to encourage discussion even in small groups of the aged. The experienced leader must remember in what ways the elderly differ from younger groups, where such presentations are sometimes a hindrance. Younger people often have had a very different kind of experience in learning to communicate feelings. Also, they frequently have been exposed from early childhood to a psychological frame of reference that may be almost unknown or at least unfamiliar to earlier generations.

Plays, Films, etc.

Plays, films and the like are particularly useful when they deal with a topic that the group members are really eager to explore but are reluctant to talk about in personal terms. Such a play or film gives the topic "emotional distance" so that discussion is possible. Or perhaps a touchy topic has already been introduced, one that is perfectly valid but that is stirring up highly charged feelings. Then the presentation of an appropriate play or film will help to universalize the problem being considered and give it the needed "safety" and objectivity.

At other times, a leader may find it difficult to help a group focus on an area of common interest and concern; the introduction of special material helps them to "settle" by providing a shared experience from which to begin. Some groups find it hard to think through problems abstractly and need to latch onto something quite specific in order to get started. Many groups go through a variety of phases; a group may have a good deal of excited discussion going for several weeks, then suddenly bog down. The use of a new approach and new material often serves to get a group moving again.

Variety of Aids

If the leader has a variety of methods and techniques, they can serve as a storehouse of approaches which may, at the right moment, enrich the discussion and help the group move on to some new level of understanding about the problems at hand. The "right" method may be one of several available. It may take the form of a planned and scheduled film showing, or it may simply involve the presentation of a poem or cartoon or newspaper item selected by the leader to bring out a point. There may be a TV series dealing with some matter that the group has been discussing and they may all decide to watch it before the next group session. Sometimes a report on a book or a movie, or a written statement of some experience or idea by one of the members, may help the group find a common focus for beginning a meeting.

Role-playing

Role-playing is another valuable technique. Informal opportunities for its use may develop spontaneously; at other times the occasion may be planned ahead. If the group has been trying to figure out why mothers-in-law may sometimes have difficulties with daughters-in-law, it might be appropriate in some groups to stop right in the middle of a discussion and suggest that a little scene be set up, with members of the group taking on the roles of family members around some definite problem involving in-law relations. If the group will be seeing a film, the leader might suggest that various members be assigned to watch particular characters, each member trying to understand what his assigned character is thinking and feeling. (This assumes that the leader has seen or knows about the film—always a good idea.) In the subsequent discussion, each member would be addressed as the person he had been asked to identify with and would be expected to respond in terms of that person's needs and feelings. Role-playing of this kind provides a way of getting inside another's feelings that all the discussion in the world may fail to approach.

Pictures and Objects

Another kind of spontaneous group experience might be developed by the leader's handing out large photographs of various family scenes —a young couple flirting or kissing, a grandparent telling a child a story, a married couple arguing, a pregnant woman and her husband in a hospital room, father leaving for work, and so forth. The pictures might be distributed to small subgroups to discuss, or each member might be given a picture and asked to tell what it reminds him of, what he thinks about this aspect of living, or what experiences or feelings he himself has had connected with such a scene. A similar technique is the one in which the leader distributes objects to the group instead of pictures—a house key, a baby bottle, a diaper-size safety pin, a penny, a school report card, a toy train or car, a doll. The group members would then be asked to share their memories and associations in relation to one object or another that makes them think of their families and their own earlier lives.

Whether one uses a formal visual aid or tries to involve the group members directly, there are certain techniques that are basic to encouraging greater participation and sensitivity to the issues. These can be reflected in all kinds of programming.

Audience Participation Methods

1. The *Feeling with* Technique: Divide the group into smaller subgroups and ask the members of each group to identify themselves with one character in a play or a film: "Pretend you are in his shoes."

2. The *Helping Person* Technique: Choose a character in a play or a film and tell the group that after the presentation the leader is going to be that particular character. The leader will ask the group, "What do you think I should have done?" "Why did I behave in that way?" "What should I do now?" "What would help me?" The leader can then also explore with the group such matters as the hazards of giving

advice, how one can give real help, and how to encourage someone to seek professional help when needed.

3. The *Camera Angle* Technique: The group is divided into subgroups that represent certain other social groups. Each member will then be expected to watch the film or play from the point of view of that group—young parents, adolescents, newcomers to the neighborhood, government officials, welfare workers, and so on. The choice of specific angles would depend on what would be appropriate to the group and to the particular presentation.

4. The *Panel Reaction* Technique: A selected group of three or four people might be asked ahead of time to discuss the material presented before the larger group. They might be asked to give their reactions, raise questions, express their point of view, or relate the material to their own life experiences. After the panel presentation the larger group would enter the discussion.

Summary

The techniques described and the use of visual aids can be especially effective in programs of mental health education for older people, who often have difficulty conceptualizing and communicating. The immediate and concrete experience frees them to share their ideas with others and in the process they develop greater ability to communicate about emotional needs. Even more important, perhaps, the use of such aids in educational discussion helps the leader avoid any attempt at probing or therapeutic intervention on a very deep level; they help keep him from going too far. These materials deal with conscious processes and can be handled with some degree of objectivity. Nevertheless, they still provide opportunities for the development of greater insight and reinforcement of healthy drives.

A few precautions should be stressed. Certainly one would not want to interrupt a good group discussion by bringing in material that might interfere with, rather than enhance, the group experience. Materials to be used with older age groups must be chosen with particular care. In work with young people, even relatively poor films and plays can often be useful. Sometimes the ones with the most unrealistic environment may stir up the most excited and meaningful discussion; poor handling of some problem situation often evokes more and better discussion than that which is too perfect and too bland. Young adults have great resilience and the leader of such groups can count on this basic strength to protect the members, if the film or play should arouse anxiety or guilt. Because older people—quite realistically—cannot look forward to a long future in which they can change, they have less resilience and must be protected from material that is likely to be threatening. Younger audiences feel that they still have time to undo things they "did wrong," to alter their ways of handling problems, to change their ideas and readjust their attitudes. They want to learn in order to grow. Older people are likely to feel that what they have done and how they have lived has created for them a situation that is final and irrevocable. A film on child care which might stir up guilt and unhappiness over "mistakes" made half a century before would clearly be an unsuitable choice. Material which relates to their *present life experiences* is therefore probably the most useful, so that whatever modifications may be inherent in it can still be carried out. To have significance and value, visual aids must be chosen as a means of providing new information and new insights that can be used within a limited future and without prompting recriminations about the past.

CHAPTER TWELVE

Implications for Programming

We believe our experience has demonstrated that mental health education discussion groups are beneficial for the aged and can form an appropriate part of many programs that serve them. Furthermore, we are convinced that they can considerably enrich the work of the host agency which provides them a setting. We feel that the information, education, support, insights and ideas for coping with life that such a series offers, add richness and meaning to existence, even for those realistically aware that their future is limited. Such programs, therefore, deserve consideration as an important part of a range of services offered to the aged.

The direction and extent to which these programs develop, however, will depend upon the priorities set by the agency; the time, training and interest of staff; the appropriateness of setting, and other factors. These, of course, vary from organization to organization. But there are alternatives for those who cannot tackle the full task of a mental health education series. The real and immediate concerns that members of our groups expressed offer many guides to program enrichment which can be applied creatively even by agencies with limited resources.

Small-Group Experience

Many small groups are focused around an activity, such as painting; a cause, such as bandage-rolling; or a process, such as selecting a nominating slate for club elections. Such programs do not necessarily evoke the same kind of personal investment as a mental health education discussion group. Nevertheless, there is a great deal to be gained from the intimacy and personal sharing of experience that small groups can provide. We found, for example, that even in clubs where members had met together for years, their knowledge of each other was frequently confined to the present, or to the problem area in their lives. They seldom knew much about the occupational, residential or educational background of their companions. At various times during our own series there was the chance to speak of these things. For example, we discovered that one member had been a missionary in Puerto Rico; as a child, another had met Buffalo Bill at a State Fair; and another had followed the Mississippi River paddle boats on a homemade raft. The response to these illustrations was a mixture of delight, surprise, amusement and incredulity. In one case, two members discovered they had had a common upbringing in the far West and left the meeting chattering like long-lost cousins.

Arranging small topical get-togethers, based on subjects such as "memories of my homeland," "why I came to the United States," or "my first job," is an appropriate way to facilitate real interchange. These programs, even with the limited goals of social exchange and improved communication, can be extremely pleasurable and meaningful to the members. Such sessions can be staffed by volunteers as well as full- or part-time personnel.

Broadening Horizons

One goal of our project was education, achieved through the direct presentation of information. At the end of a series, members often spoke of how much they had learned and how much they had enjoyed being part of a learning group. This suggests the possibility of more educational programs within the group-centered agency. Learning with tests, grades, prepared papers and the like may or may not be threatening, but learning through exposure to new and stimulating information is obviously as welcome and exciting in the later years as it is at any other stage of life.

Sessions to help older people learn about city government, the culture of a local minority group, comparative religion, horticulture, general science and natural history, arranged in cooperation with authoritative speakers and with the use of demonstrations and field trips, might well be feasible and would provide interesting supplements to existing programs.

Intergeneration Programs

In their discussions of happiness, the elderly talked about their need for involvement with people of other ages. They spoke of the boredom and depression which result from being arbitrarily confined to their own age group. Not every elderly person finds it difficult to extend his circle to include younger persons; but there are many isolated, unsophisticated people who do. Many of the latter type are members of clubs and centers which could provide immediate access to younger people within their own buildings or through their own auspices. However, our experience has shown that too often agencies tend to operate completely independent programs that never touch each other or, at best, consider mixing age groups only during occasional token activities such as Christmas parties, when one group may serve or entertain another.

In order to be most meaningful, intergroup activities should be integral, sustained parts of the program. At every stage of life, there is real satisfaction to be gained from helping others, and this warm human instinct has a good deal of potential for program application. Youngsters in a nursery enjoy giving the things they make to someone who will fuss over them; grade-school youngsters adore audiences for their amateur dramatics; teen-agers gain security and pride through service—for example, painting a mural on the wall of an adult lounge; young adults looking for causes with which to identify might want to examine the social problems of the elderly.

Such programs can be taken one step further. The nursery school youngsters enjoy a singing or music session *with* the golden-age group; the grade school youngsters might enjoy a cooking session *led* by them; the teen-agers might work *side by side* on a mural with mature painters; and the young adults might *work together* with the elderly on some social action activity. The gamut of program opportunities is wide, and there are numerous things that can be done for the mutual benefit of all groups. The principle of age-mixing has to be seriously considered and planned for, however, as part of an on-going service if it is to have the added real value or effect upon the community image of the older person.

Another stimulus to inter-age-group activity for club members could be developed through their own comrades who belong to community organizations which welcome all adults. A Golden Age Club alone cannot be expected to meet all the social needs of its constituents, and members should be encouraged to seek other outlets. Those who hesitate to go to new places alone can be helped and stimulated by the support of the more able, who could be enlisted to serve as companions and guides for the first visit to a church or benevolent group function, a lecture or a film series.

In every community there are schools, libraries, settlements, religious organizations and institutions for the sick or homeless where older people can make a contribution. Often, at present, access to these groups is not easy, but constructive change could be initiated through community effort stimulated by the staffs of organizations having a primary concern for the aging.

Programs Related to the Role of Grandparent

Most older people who are grandparents initially feel sincere joy, anticipation, pride and satisfaction in seeing the family line perpetuated. These feelings may become diluted when there is little opportunity for personal contact or communication, or when grandchildren become more independent. Members complained most, however, about the change in these initial happy feelings when they tried to determine what role they might fill beyond that of giver of love and gifts. With this as a starting point, workers can do a great deal to strengthen, interpret and add meaning to the grandparent's role.

We have previously referred to the grandparents' confusion about acting as disciplinarian. This could be examined through discussion, along with their appropriate roles as teacher of skills, language, family tradition and culture; the link with the past and image of the future; developer of feelings of filial responsibility; friend and companion. The discussion would, of course, serve only as a first step. Whatever action might result would be up to the individual member within the confines of his own family structure. However, club programs other than discussions can also add importance to this role. Groups of children or individual youngsters who are not related to the members might serve as extensions of their own grandchildren. Potentially responsive youngsters can be contacted through such agencies as schools, hospitals, orphanages, churches or synagogues, nursery schools and community centers.

In one agency, group discussions led to a decision to start a baby-sitting service for working mothers. In another, the sessions on the importance of the grandparent's role and on the richness in their individual history and background convinced members they had a contribution to make to the young. When the series ended, they were still in the throes of deciding who the recipients of such service should be and where and how to get started, but they were headed in the right direction.

Before groups such as these can act as "grandparents" in a day nursery or public library, complicated administrative arrangements may have to be worked out. Agency staffs must—at present—carry a good deal of responsibility for getting such programs off the ground, and we believe they should accept this pioneering role with the hope that some day these extended opportunities for expression will become widespread.

Before concluding consideration of this general area of activity, a word of caution may be in order. Although it is true that many older people want and need more contact with children and younger adults, there are some who do not and many who can enjoy only limited and structured relationships with them. Some of these persons already have more contacts than they can enjoy in large families or crowded households; a few may simply not be attuned to children, while others are so involved in meeting the adjustment problems of later life that active relationships with younger people are simply disconcerting distractions. This may be unfortunate but it is often true. In creating opportunities for intergeneration activities, then, staff must keep in mind the continuing need for separate activities as well. And older persons who, for whatever reason, are not ready or do not wish to mix with younger people should not be made to feel like hopeless old fogeys in consequence.

Programs Designed To Encourage Friendships

Within the confines of clubs and centers we met many old-timers and steady-attenders who, theoretically, should have "found" each other in these settings. Some did. But many others, discussions revealed, need special structured help aimed at developing friendships. Even when surrounded by the same people day after day—playing cards, eating lunch, working at crafts and so forth—many members still considered the others acquaintances rather than friends. To overcome this difficulty, programs can be designed that foster deeper involvement among the members by offering opportunities for real communication and active enjoyment, a chance to give as well as receive, ways to develop and share mutual interests. A specific educational approach may be needed that can be used in developing such discussion programs. What do you want in a friendship? How do you make a friend? How do you keep one? These are questions which help some members realize that they must make an investment of themselves in order to help friendships begin.

For example, Mrs. M told one group how she had pursued a friendship with Mr. S. She took the lead in stimulating conversation, suggested they share their cafeteria meals at the same table, asked his protection as escort home after an evening meeting. She said she knew he was without a TV set and invited him to watch a show. Women in the group who regarded this initially as boldness began to understand through discussion that the shy Mr. S, whose need for a friend was no less than Mrs. M's, would not have found himself a partner in such a mutually satisfying arrangement had she not acted as she did.

People living in huge housing projects often said they didn't know anyone on the same floor. They seemed overwhelmed by the suggestion that they might invite neighbors to tea as a way of introducing themselves. Agency staffs working in cooperation with social workers, housing managers and recreational therapists might well consider the possibilities of organizing such events on a group basis as a way of helping elderly tenants make initial efforts at neighborliness and friendship.

The same kind of caution suggested in regard to intergeneration activities bears consideration here also. Particularly in cities, many people of all ages are content with superficial relationships and avoid the involvements of deeper friendship. Others may have gradually developed "shells" of varying degrees of thickness as the result of disappointments and hurtful rebuffs or exploitation of their openness and generosity. Still others may have suffered a series of painful losses of close companions and do not wish to risk further loss. The sensitive leader, in encouraging older persons to give of themselves more freely, will recognize that the hesitancy some reveal may be based on painful past experience. He will not attempt to push them faster than they can go or feel let down if they do not want to change their ways.

Activities To Restore Accountability

To be accountable means to be responsible and answerable for certain deeds in the eyes of others. Being freed of accountability can be a relief for a while, but on a full-time basis it tends to dehumanize existence and makes for loss of self-esteem (if nobody depends on you, you don't mean much to anyone). Many group members were overburdened by a sense of no longer being needed and did not know how to cope with their loss. Only a child, they felt, can be permitted to play all day; accountability is the mark of adult status. To differentiate themselves from children, many older people feel the need for regular tasks, individually defined as important, through which they can experience accountability and responsibility.

For some, accountability will come through helping the group by watering the plants, checking clothing or setting the tables for snacks. In most centers these simple tasks are recognized as work that members can perform. But there are many whose intelligence, drive and experience equip them for a deeper involvement which is sometimes difficult to achieve. There are, however, many quasi-administrative details which these able members could handle. Some are prepared, or could be trained, to relieve a receptionist or telephone operator, for instance; to help with mimeographing or typing; to assist a volunteer leader, and so forth. There are some who can be involved in even broader ways, such as contacting community resources, representing the agency as part of a group at a meeting, or working in another agency in cooperation with their club.

Much as many older persons want this feeling of being needed, and vital as it is to supply suitable outlets and opportunities, it must be remembered that within this age group (as well as in younger groups) there are those whose full energies are taken up simply in meeting their own needs and personal responsibilities. Some may be in the first stages of enjoying freedom from lifelong duties to others, and a minority may have done little for others at any time of life. When drawing members into action, leaders would do well to remember that, as in other stages of life, it is often those who are already the busiest who feel most sharply the call to serve and that those who have leaned heavily on others for years will continue to do so without a qualm. The leader should be careful not to overburden the former or feel undue disappointment at the "let George do it" attitude of the latter. He should individualize his expectations and focus on helping those in the large middle area work their way back to responsible giving, to enjoy the opportunities for growth and personal satisfaction this achievement brings.

Relationship to Reality Pressures

Members of senior citizens' clubs and centers know that in such settings they can expect to find acceptance and concern for them as individuals. Besides providing opportunities for socialization, some organizations are prepared as well to give specialized services, either directly or in cooperation with other agencies, or by referral to appropriate sources of help.

Since few, other than those who work with the elderly, tend to see them as a group or to know them and their problems intimately, it is logical that impetus for increased special services on their behalf should come from such organizations. In their concern for the "whole" man, agency staffs face a unique task. It cannot be minimized. Fulfilling it will require the same kind of stamina, foresight and courage which social welfare pioneers such as Jane Addams employed. The services lacking for all groups in need—including children, unwed mothers, the chronically ill and handicapped—force us to realize that it will take time, patience and persistence to achieve better services for the aged. The fact that most existing programs have come about through the efforts and diligence of special interest groups underscores the need for concerted action.

Housing

The area of housing, particularly public housing, is one where a great deal of work has been done; yet much remains still to be accomplished. In New York City, we have witnessed an increase in the percentage of housing allotted to the elderly, and more consideration for appropriate architectural adjustments. In conjunction with housing experts, social agencies have been consulted on physical needs and services to be incorporated in housing plans. Appropriate officials have met with groups of older citizens to discuss suggestions resulting from the latter's own knowledge and experience. A good deal of thought has been given to the question of age-integrated projects versus separate accommodations for this group largely because of concerns voiced by the aged themselves.

In our discussions, group members mentioned the burden of anonymity they often feel as tenants in large public or private housing developments. This anonymity engenders certain fears. Workers with the aging need to use imagination and skill in bringing such fears into the open and in planning programs to reduce them. Setting up floor organizations and the installation of a concierge in large apartment dwellings are examples of attempts to solve this problem. The need for telephones to meet emergencies and to provide means of contact with the outside community was another recurrent concern mentioned in discussion groups. The special urgency of this need on the part of older adults must be recognized.

Multiple dwellings in slum areas where the elderly may have resided for twenty to forty years are often characterized by overcrowding, poorly lit and ill-kept stairwells, antiquated plumbing and cracked plaster—all contributing to discouragement and a lack of concern about maintenance among tenants. The social agency has a legitimate role to play in helping neighbors develop a sense of home and community responsibility, by working both with landlords and with neighbors to improve conditions. Utopia is not necessarily the goal; but certainly there is much to be done so long as even one 80-year-old woman must climb five flights of stairs to get to her apartment. And must mount a chair in order to enter the double kitchen sink which serves as a bathtub!

Health

The extent of the health needs of the elderly is staggering, although metropolitan areas across the country have made some gains in providing needed resources, especially for the indigent. We are learning, however, that many of the emotional problems which surround ill health often limit the full use of such facilities. Sometimes the more extensive the service, the more difficult it is to use—witness the long delays before a doctor can be seen, the long periods of standing in line to have prescriptions filled, the need to travel to strange and sometimes distant areas for specialized services, and so on.

During discussion meetings many complaints were expressed about health services. In one group particularly, these complaints seemed to reflect anger, fear, disrespect, misinformation and lack of information. To clarify this situation, a mass meeting—open to the entire community—was planned with the group.

At this meeting members were able to raise many questions about their health services directly with the local administrators equipped to answer them and, possibly, in a position to make changes. Even if nothing else resulted from the meeting, the fact that responsible officials were made more aware of patients' difficulties can be seen as a constructive achievement. Furthermore, members learned from the session about the extensive services of a local health center which they had not been using to advantage.

But ignorance of health resources or dissatisfactions with them are not the only deterrents to good care. A sensitive agency director, aware of the fact that older people share the same fears, hesitancies and apathy which hold back people of all ages from having regular physical examinations, attempted to meet the problem by creating a group project. As a result, at the termination of the discussion series, arrangements were being made to enroll members for group visits to the health center for standard diabetes and X-ray examinations. Thus group support was mobilized to promote use of individual services.

A leader attempting such group action, however, should be alert to signs of real resistance. Realistic past experience of some members may have led to hostility or fear of doctors and hospitals that is deeply rooted. Differences of opinion exist even among geriatricians themselves and some older persons have reason to hesitate before becoming involved in procedures that may lead to extended tests and treatments. This is a difficult area for discussion and signs of real resistance should not be written off as mere indications of ignorance or misinformation. Group support should not be permitted to become group pressure.

Practical action can help to allay one frequent source of anxiety—that which stems from a fear of becoming ill and not having any one person to turn to for special help. Although visiting committees for the sick had long been a part of basic agency program, the center realized they did not fully meet this need. A "friendship file" was therefore developed formalizing an arrangement whereby two appropriate persons became reasonably responsible for each other. One kept an eye on the other and could be called upon in case of emergency.

Money

Attitudes toward finances have been mentioned. Members consistently expressed positive attitudes about Social Security and the proposed medical care provisions through the Social Security program;

they expressed negative attitudes about public welfare, charity and dependency on children. Agencies that deal with large groups of older people are in a position to call public attention to their needs and sentiments. Service agencies can be a community force for action aimed at enhancing the dignity and self-respect of those who find themselves financially indigent. Are organizations with boards of directors doing all they can to educate board members in this area or helping them to use their influence appropriately? Are we helping those members who receive public assistance to recognize their own role as possible agents of change? Are we making use of all the information we have?

Answers to such questions must arise out of an awareness of the problems and a willingness to admit that services for the aging are a matter of concern for all.

Community Attitudes

There is a new dilemma facing Americans today that is more serious than many of us care to acknowledge. Medical and technological advances are making old age a more common reality. Not only are we more likely to become old by our current definition, but to live many years in a state of old age. How ironic it is to "progress" to a point at which people become uncomfortable and afraid! Yet progress it is, and the irony rests in our inability to use and accept it. Many of the same attitudes which existed when "the later years" connoted the fifties and sixties rather than the seventies and eighties are still prevalent. This lag between public attitudes and current fact is correctly perceived by our elders.

We found that the people we worked with often were willing and able to adapt to their changed status but were handicapped by public attitudes. For example, many did not want to work any longer because of physical and emotional strain involved and, furthermore, were well aware that the industrial world no longer had a place for them. Yet they would say they felt ashamed in the eyes of others because they were unemployed. Those who do accommodate themselves to this conflict must often struggle with all kinds of rationalizations in order to endure it.

Not only is our present generation of older people affected, but all those who follow will suffer similarly unless we begin to reorient our thinking. We need to find ways to help people consciously recognize that they too will be old some day, that old age can be a meaningful time of life, and that they can begin to prepare themselves for it in their middle years. All community-based agencies such as the schools, libraries and neighborhood centers, as well as agencies for the aged, have a role to play here.

Some Golden Age Clubs have had meaningful programs with the children of their members, attempting to develop awareness and sensitivity to problems of the older adult. Fraternal organizations, labor unions and educational institutions have organized seminars and lecture programs. We must continue to use every available device to reach people on this issue; and, to be effective, the program must be long-range.

Most young people say old age begins arbitrarily at 65. To the elderly we met, "old" meant bedridden. Whatever the case—and this is relatively unimportant—we should recognize that there are many positive elements in being old. We can learn about these from older people and can use this information in teaching and affecting others.

When one thinks about the potential early in life for shaping positive attitudes toward old age and the elderly, it is apparent that teaching children to help aged persons across the street falls somewhat short of a comprehensive approach. The Council Center for Senior Citizens, a project of the Brooklyn, N. Y., Section of the National Council of Jewish Women, assumed a broader viewpoint in September 1962 as part of its community service program. The Council's goals included the creation of opportunities for the aged to give constructive service related to community life outside the Center. The project was established in cooperation with a local public elementary school where Center members volunteered under the supervision of the teaching staff to sew costumes and graduation gowns, help publish the school newspaper, assist in the library and woodwork shop, judge art and science exhibits, and provide entertainment for auditorium programs. One such program, presented to children of 12 and 13, was a Gay

Nineties Revue. The following are excerpts from letters the youngsters wrote in response to the experience:

It is most inspiring to see our senior citizens possess such vitality. . . . You showed us that the older generation is still very active. . . . You and the rest of the "stars" really acted like professional performers straight from Hollywood. . . . I understand the importance of a community where young and old alike share in the responsibilities and pleasures of belonging. The idea of more frequent visits to our school by the members of your club for various reasons promises to be quite rewarding. . . . It really takes courage sometimes to try to be nice to the younger generation. I suppose it's because we might think you're too old. . . . The way the senior ladies and men sang and danced, one would think they were about 20. . . .

Besides being entertaining, it showed older people enjoy life too and that they are not ready for the rocking chair. . . . It has made us realize that senior citizens can be as useful and productive as any young person. . . . It is comforting to know that there is still a place for all the people whose children are probably married and have forgotten them. . . . The senior citizens' ambitious ideas to contribute to assistance of our school is most worthy of commendation. May you and all the senior citizens, not only in Kings County, but throughout the nation, strive to accomplish this purpose. . . .

It is obvious that this program must have a powerful positive potential when, after the first major contact, youngsters can talk with tenderness and sensitivity about the need of people of all ages to "share in the responsibilities and pleasures of belonging."

Programs in which different generations actually work side by side help to shape the child's general attitude toward the aging. But they can also go beyond that to touch his teachers, his siblings, his parents and his assessment of his own grandparents. In view of the lack of importance many older people attach to their grandparent role, this could be one very significant aspect of such a program. The means to accomplish such results are available; the opportunities are all around us. Do we really look for them and use them with the vigor we employ in other programs?

Possibilities for Direct Action

Are we doing all we can to help older people help themselves through knowledge of the issues in local and national legislation? Is there a role to play in encouraging the use of good health services and working for the improvement and extension of others? Can we help interpret medical aid programs to the aged so that they may be used to greater advantage?

Can the Center serve low-cost meals, help members learn about the value of nutrition and inexpensive foods, or start a meals-on-wheels program for its homebound? What about inexpensive vacation opportunities? Is the high cost of carfare or limited transportation a serious concern in your community? Is there a fraction of the membership which needs help in finding suitable employment opportunities? Are agencies available to them or could you start a new one? In other words, do our programs really reveal broad concern for the people they serve? Are there realistic ways to do more than is being done?

Professionally trained staff members have a particular responsibility to give leadership in this area, since their education is designed to provide them with special understanding of the concerns of their clients. Such understanding must be carefully applied to a system of priorities, so that this talent does not get diluted in tasks which can be performed by volunteers or less highly trained staff. Each of us also needs to ask himself: Is it really the burden of staff shortage which inhibits the scope of our program, or have we become preoccupied with activity which we have come to think of as important but which is actually limited—and limiting—in scope?

And in Conclusion . . .

We have tried here to emphasize the vital importance of acknowledging the older person's adulthood and desire for autonomy. The aged are—in the fullest sense of the term—mature individuals involved in the difficult, far-too-seldom pleasant, struggle which we call life. No matter how discouraged or frustrated some may be, they know their own worth. They must be approached with dignity and respect. Much of the success of the mental health education groups described can be attributed to this attitude alone, since the communication of such regard often stimulated involvement even before members understood the true nature and intent of the series. And it was this approach which eventually permitted people to express their concerns and consider practical plans for action.

Mental health education discussion groups constitute one approach to an important aspect of the challenge of the aged. We think these groups are practical and feasible to operate within most existing agency structures. Whether we continue to use this approach or to find new ones, however, is not nearly as important as recognizing that the age of innocence in working with the elderly is over. They have come of age in our society, if only by virtue of numbers alone. In their numbers, they represent a powerful and extensive source of patience, strength and courage. They have begun to express themselves. We have teased them just enough with the concept that the later years can be "golden" years, and at the same time have failed to supply enough means or opportunity. Some now want to take up this challenge. Not only their future but the future of all of us is involved; it demands that we share in the responsibility for meeting this challenge. In this work, we should be motivated by the belief that in an age of new frontiers our modern wonders become meaningless without the assurance that we can expect to live *all* the years of our lives with a sense of self-respect, purpose, hope and fulfillment. With our help and understanding today's aged can show us the way.

About the Experiment That
Came First

Needs and Uncertainties

The youngest was 59 and the oldest was 87. The majority were in their seventies. For years they had worked to make a living, maintain a home, rear their families. Their days had been filled with the responsibilities and rewards, the sorrows and satisfactions, the pleasures and problems that come with an active involvement in life.

Now most of them were alone—wife or husband dead, children too far away for regular visiting. They ate and slept in furnished rooms or boarding houses or struggled to keep up with apartments much too large for them. Golden Age Clubs, senior citizens' centers, offered them a place to go, things to do, people to talk with. But even those whose family ties were still intact felt the need of something more than this, and they weren't sure what it was. Being old was a new experience for these men and women—as it will be in time for more and more of us—and it brought questions for which they had no answers. Despite the wide range of studies recently completed or currently under way on various aspects of life in the later years, no specialist had answers for them, either.

In the fall of 1961, these same questions brought these men and women together as participants in the first of a series of discussion groups that comprised a two-year demonstration project on mental health education. This book is one of the outcomes of that project. In a sense, these men and women demanded that it be produced, and it could not have been produced without their participation. This is an account of the project itself, its development and organization, its major findings and their general significance. The chapters that precede are intended as a guide for those in a position to use the discussion group approach with other groups of older people. We trust that our experience, as set forth here, will lead them to feel, as we do, that this form of mental health education can be used successfully with the elderly in many more settings and situations than we were able to work in.

The project proper was conceived by the Manhattan Society for Mental Health and carried out by its staff with the help of a grant from the Aaron E. Norman Fund. Realization of the need for such an effort had, of course, developed some time earlier. To understand how this came about, one must know something about the sponsoring agency itself.

Preliminary Experiences

The Manhattan Society for Mental Health is a service-oriented mental health association but its aim goes beyond service alone. The mental health needs of Manhattan, which is in the heart of one of the world's largest and most complicated cities, are served by a multiplicity of agencies, most of them with some actual or potential value for mental health services but by no means adequate to the enormous need. What the Society does is to maintain close contact with the community's real-life problems, gain added insights into the needs of the population, and in the process spot whatever gaps or inadequacies exist in current services. It can then develop new or different methods of approach, demonstrate and evaluate these methods, and—when their usefulness has been proved—present them in a way that will have constructive impact on the program of other agencies with on-going services.

In recent years, requests from community groups for mental health education services have revealed a steadily increasing need to develop more and better help for the aged. The demand has been expressed often in a simple request for "a speaker." But when staff from the

Society, in response to such requests, met with these older groups and the people who were trying to help them—for example, in a retired workers' local of a union or in a senior citizens' center—it became evident from the members' responses that they wanted something more than the experience of passive audience. They seemed to be grasping for an opportunity to participate actively in some different kind of program, one that would give them the chance not only to gain information but also to develop their own thoughts together as a group; even, perhaps, to act in accordance with decisions reached through their discussions.

Perception of the Need

As visitors to many of these settings also, it was possible for our staff members to view with an outsider's perspective the activities in which these older persons were engaged; and it appeared to us that in their eagerness for new experience these men and women were expressing dissatisfaction with the limited nature of many of the activities arranged for them. Basket-weaving, ceramics, bridge clubs were not enough. The older people themselves, as well as those working with them, were becoming increasingly concerned with the multiple and interrelated aspects of this stage of life, were beginning to seek new resources for help in meeting the problems and challenges it presented. Both group members and program staffs, therefore, eagerly accepted the offer of a discussion leader when all they had requested was a speaker.

Early Trials

In these early experiments, limited to a single meeting, it was decided to focus on the crisis of adjustment to a new stage in life. Some general observations were prepared on the availability of information about the "ages and stages" of childhood and on the lack of thought given up until now to the fact that human beings face changes, new challenges and adjustments all through life. Adults, too, the discussion leader pointed out, go through dramatic shifts in roles. Perhaps greater understanding and awareness of how these changes affect us might

help us to meet them more perceptively and successfully. Some of
these points of change or crisis occur when we leave school, go to
work, marry and become parents. As parents we meet new challenges
as each child enters a new stage of growth, after which we discover
still more adjustments to be made as we become in-laws and grandparents. Finally we face the changes forced by widowhood, retirement, physical slowing-down and disabilities.

These aspects of growth and change were mentioned briefly in 10-
to 20-minute talks at single-meeting assignments. The presentation
was kept as informal as possible. It was pointed out that many of these
subjects, touching as they did on important personal experiences, involved deep feelings. Therefore, we could profit most from our examination of them by discussing them freely and informally with each
other.

Settings for Early Experiments

One of the first things we observed was that the response to this
approach was quite similar even in widely dissimilar settings. The following represent a composite of the differences in settings for our early
experiences:

1. A Golden Age Club in a well-established community center had
knowledgeable and dedicated staff workers who were quite clear about
what they wanted and had been able to help the group articulate its
needs before the meeting. Approximately 30 members attended. The
group met around a table in a comfortable and cheerful room. Most of
the members knew each other quite well, but there were between five
and ten new people present. The speaker was introduced in a pleasant
and accurate way, and the group seemed to expect some discussion, if
not as much as the speaker anticipated. This was in a lower-middle-
class neighborhood, with many foreign-born, mostly of Central European background.

2. A newer center, administered by one semiprofessional worker,
was staffed by a harassed and inadequate group of nonprofessional
assistants who were desperately looking for programs. They had no

clear goals nor had they any definite idea of their purpose in calling for a mental health "speaker." About 30 members were working on a mailing in a large room at four or five separate tables. The center director simply announced, "Here's a lady from the Mental Health to talk with you. You can go on working on the mailing, but try to keep quiet, so you can hear her." This center was also in a lower-middle-class neighborhood, with a basically Jewish population but with some influx of Negroes.

3. This was a meeting planned by the staff member in charge of an extensive union educational program. About 50 to 75 were present, in a medium-sized lecture hall; some knew each other, many did not. This was the only group in our series whose members were all women. The meeting had received good publicity, and the members had a great deal to do with the planning. The speaker was introduced by a member of the program committee, with charm, humor and poise.

Evidences of Need

In each of these diverse situations the group members looked uncomfortable at first about participating. The opening remarks brought a great deal of head-shaking agreement on the neglected "ages and stages" of later life and the mental health problems and needs of older people. Discussion was slow to get started, but when it did, the floodgates seemed to open. The articulate and moving contributions and the deep feelings expressed revealed quite clearly a sense of desperate urgency for talking about immediate experiences and emotions.

When reactions such as these were reported and discussed in staff conferences at the Manhattan Society for Mental Health, it was agreed that these meetings indicated there was a far larger job to be done. In these single meetings, group members had raised profound and searching questions. The scope of subjects ranged widely, covering relations with children and grandchildren, housing problems, health problems and fears of disability and dependence, feelings of unworthiness and uselessness, the wide gap between felt needs and available community resources, fears about becoming mentally ill, and a host of other pressing concerns. It was clear that more time was needed to permit people to explore their expressed concerns more fully.

An Early Discussion Series

Shortly thereafter a request for a speaker for a single meeting came from a sensitive and very able director of a Department of Welfare center for older people. This seemed an appropriate setting in which to experiment with a series of meetings, and our request to do this was greeted with genuine enthusiasm. The cooperation received in this first experimental group had a great deal to do with the development of the total project. Our plan was to hold a series of four weekly meetings, focused on "Emotional Adjustment to the Later Years of Life." Members of the center would be invited to participate, with the understanding that this was not a set of individual lectures but a workshop series offering a great deal of group discussion. The center director recruited the group, interpreted its purpose, and also participated actively in the discussions.

About 40 members attended the first session, meeting in a classroom. After that, average attendance was about 20 to 25, despite the fact that the series started in the middle of the winter during a period of very cold weather and heavy snowfall. The center had a heterogeneous membership made up primarily of Negroes, Puerto Ricans, Italians and Germans. Most had been unskilled and semiskilled workers; all were retired.

This series was continued for five sessions, and the conclusion of all involved was that the methods and techniques used in mental health education discussion groups lent themselves admirably to work with older people. Members of the group, known to the center to be troubled in many ways, seemed to gain support and comfort and to have the healthier aspects of their personalities strengthened through the group experience. One of the most interesting effects of the series was that on the activities in the center itself as program development was enhanced. It was made more meaningful by the kind of information brought to staff attention by the discussions. A new spirit seemed to prevail.

Demonstration Project Drafted

With the encouragement and support of the center director and our own increasing enthusiasm for the potentials in this kind of program, we developed a proposal for a two-year demonstration project to explore further the possibilities of developing and refining the discussion group method for use with senior citizens. We recognized that if this approach to mental health education was to prove of genuine value, we had to know much more about appropriate new techniques and about modifications that might be necessary in techniques used with other age groups. We had to learn more about older people themselves and about the kinds of settings in which such groups might be useful.

With our grant from the Aaron E. Norman Fund, supplemented by the Society's funds and staff, the project proper began in the fall of 1961. Staff included Sylvan S. Furman, executive director of the Manhattan Society for Mental Health, who designed and directed the project; Wilma Klein, as social group worker; Mrs. Eda J. LeShan, formerly the Society's director of education, as educational consultant and leader of the preliminary demonstration series; and Guido M. Crocetti, assistant professor at the Johns Hopkins University School of Hygiene and Public Health, as research consultant. Miss Klein's time over a period of two years was devoted to this project and the case material cited throughout this book is drawn from her work. Mr. Crocetti adapted and analyzed the results of attitude surveys administered to some of the groups in early stages of the project. Dr. Alvin I. Goldfarb, psychiatric consultant on aging to the New York State Department of Mental Hygiene, was consulted on technical questions early in the project.

Groups Selected

The initial task was to organize a series of experimental groups, keeping in mind the many questions we hoped to explore. We sought a variety of groups, in different kinds of agencies, in different economic, ethnic, social, geographical and cultural settings, with people representing as wide a cross section as possible. The final selection fell short in some respects—the range of economic levels, for example, was somewhat narrower than we might have hoped—but in other ways it provided variations and challenges we could not have anticipated, such as the wide range of differences in activities, personnel, and general *esprit de corps* among the individual agencies worked with.

The final selection included several agencies whose earlier requests for speakers we had not been able to meet at the time; centers where we had provided a single lecture and where interest in continuing had been great, and agencies which seemed to respond with interest to our initial offer of such a service. Contacts were established with more than a dozen potential centers. Some had to be eliminated, however, for such practical reasons as lack of space, language limitations of the membership, or organizational problems within the agency.

Approach to Center Directors

In each case, the group worker discussed with the center director the background of our interest, our general goals and the various possibilities we felt there might be in developing mental health discussion groups for older people—namely, as a service to the center's own members, as a source of information to people working with the elderly, and as a source of information and guidance in future program planning for such centers. Emphasis was placed on our wish to cooperate very closely with the agency personnel, to enrich their work if we could, and to supplement their programs. Certainly we would do nothing to compete with them or to increase their difficulties and problems. We stressed how much we valued the privilege and opportunity their cooperation furnished us and emphasized our wish to share the experience with them as fully as possible, with the hope that whatever we might learn might in turn be of use to them.

Setting the Stage

In beginning work with almost every group, we found that it was important to interpret the role of the mental health association to the director very carefully, and that reinterpretation was necessary at the beginning of each of the first sessions. No matter how careful the center director was in outlining the purpose of the group, the fact that the leader came from the mental health society seemed to produce many misconceptions in the minds of the members. Over and over again, the emphasis on mental *health* had to be presented. These groups, we stressed, were not going to "analyze" or treat mental illness, or teach psychological theories about mental illness. As in the single-session meetings, we pointed out the need for adults to adjust to new stages of life and explained that together, members of the group would have an opportunity to explore their own feelings and experiences in order to bring greater understanding to their own relationships and living situations. As simply and directly as possible, we attempted to convey the hope that such group discussion could help the members to rediscover, explore and use existing strengths to raise the level of their social and emotional functioning above that of mere existence.

Agencies Selected

Eventually, five agencies were selected to participate in the project. The center directors were asked to handle the recruitment and selection of group members, keeping in mind that we hoped to have the participants come regularly and that we wanted a normal, average, representative group. We asked that the directors use their own judgment in screening out those who might not benefit from such a group experience—for example, those with language or hearing difficulties, those with severe emotional problems or a history of mental illness, and people who did not attend the centers with any regularity. The number of sessions was left open—we wanted to see what would develop—but we suggested that the series might last from about 6 to 15 sessions, with decisions about ending the series to be arrived at in consultation with the center staff. Content of the meetings was left unstructured, to be developed by the group, with the leader actively participating in this process.

The groups were formed at the following centers and met as indicated:

—The Yorkville Neighborhood Club at the 92nd Street YM and YWHA (10 weekly sessions)

—The East Harlem Day Center of the Department of Welfare at East 109th Street (13 sessions)

—The Elliot Neighbors Club, at Hudson Guild Settlement House, jointly sponsored by Department of Welfare, Chelsea area (9 sessions)

—The Little White Door, at the Isabella Home, Department of Welfare (13 sessions)

—Washington Heights Inwood YM and YWHA (5 sessions)

Most of these groups had an average attendance ranging from 15 to 40 people. The majority attended two or more sessions. A total of 15 men and 39 women attended more than half of the sessions in a series. Other meetings, not in series, were held at:

—William Hodson Center, Department of Welfare Day Center, approximately 30 present

—Wright Park Community Center, Department of Parks, 60 to 75 present

—District #65, Retail, Wholesale Department Store Union, AFL-CIO (3 sessions), 35 to 50 present

—Lenox Hill Neighborhood Association, approximately 20 present

—Goddard-Riverdale Neighborhood Center, approximately 30 present

—Yorkville Neighbors Club, 92nd Street YM and YWHA, 50 to 60 present

—East Harlem (demonstration series, 1960), 30 to 40 present at one or more of five sessions

Since we were called upon to speak at other single meetings as well, we estimate roughly that, including the preliminary work, we had contact and discussion with approximately 500 older people.

Composition of the Groups

Each group session in a series was approximately one and one-half to two hours in length, meeting weekly. The range in members' ages was from 59 to 87. The median age of those attending regularly (and all the following figures apply to that segment) was approximately 73 years. The large majority were retired and had retired during the past two- to five-year period. As for marital status, the widowed were the largest number, with single persons next. A minority were married. Two were separated. There were no divorced persons. As for other family ties, only a few of the group members had children or grandchildren living near enough for any real contact. This, of course, reflected the urban setting and the movement of population out of the core city.

Members' Living Conditions, Health and Support

The large majority of members lived alone, about 50 per cent of these in furnished rooms and boarding houses, the rest in their own apartments. Approximately half the group had been attending the club for one year or less; a quarter for two to five years and the rest for more than five years. Fewer than half had been officers or committee members of the club at any time. More than 90 per cent of the members were very regular in their attendance at the centers. Approximately 50 per cent were considered to be in reasonably good health, 25 per cent had a history of serious illness, hospitalization or handicap, and 25 per cent were regularly attending clinics for some chronic condition. A large majority of members were living on Social Security and on welfare benefits. There was a small sprinkling getting major financial support from a union pension fund. The fewest were living entirely on independent income or on aid from friends or relatives. In most cases there was a combination of several sources of income.

We mention these figures only to provide a rough frame of reference. Information was obtained informally; in some cases it could not be fully ascertained or carefully checked for accuracy. However, limited as this information may be, it does seem to suggest a few tentative generalizations, which were borne out by informal observation. In all cases, the majority of those who attended regularly seemed to represent the more isolated segments of the group—the widowed or single, living alone—as well as those without children and grandchildren nearby. These persons seemed to be more dependent on the club as the center of their social experiences. Those who attended more irregularly may be a very different group in many ways. In the absence of specific figures on these differences, our feeling is that in many instances those with more active and satisfying lives tended to drop out more often, but this observation was never tested in any way and of course there were many exceptions.

Factors of Social Class

Working in neighborhood community centers tended to provide an aging population of lower socioeconomic status than might be most fruitful for gaining a balanced view of old age problems generally. However, we feel that this was not a real handicap. For one thing, we wanted to find ways of reaching people *in real need*. Secondly, we found that whenever we did have opportunity to meet with groups of higher social, economic or educational background, very much the same concerns were raised; while the forms of self-expression might vary, the themes remained quite remarkably constant. At first we had wondered whether or not the real-life pressures on people struggling for survival might tend to diminish a concern with emotional problems: Do these problems come up more in middle and upper-middle-class groups, where immediate and practical needs are being met more adequately? Nothing in our experience suggests that they do. We found concern about housing and health in middle-class groups, and concern about interpersonal relationships with children and grandchildren just as frequently in lower-class groups.

Having now worked intensively with five groups, and with added information supplied by a number of single meetings in a variety of settings, we feel that a body of practical information has evolved. Some group discussion techniques have proved more successful than others; certain kinds of content came up again and again, and needed to be handled in different ways under different circumstances. The centers in which we worked played a vital role in the general usefulness of the discussion groups, and we think we have learned some of the ways in which such groups can be best utilized as part of a total program for the aged. Of course it was the group members themselves who helped us most, with new information and insights into their problems and possibilities, and the richness of their wisdom and sensitivity helped us to see new facets of mental health in the later years.

Staff Conferences

To reinforce and broaden the impact of the work done directly with these groups, conferences were held both with the personnel of the host agencies, and with representatives of other agencies where, because of limited staff time or for other reasons, it was not possible to conduct discussion series. Conferences with host agency staff members were usually on an individual basis, following sessions with their group members, or at other times, and they also were afforded opportunities to observe discussions.

A considerable number of agencies where discussions were not held were served through the medium of periodic, all-day workshop conferences, where there were presentations by the Society's staff and general discussion. The response of the participants was uniformly and spontaneously enthusiastic. These conferences were separately recorded and are not reported here. It is a source of regret to us that because of limited staff time it was not possible to hold more of these conferences during the two years of the project.

Moving Ahead

It is our hope that our experience will serve to enrich the information and understanding of others working with the aged, and that many of these workers will want to develop discussion groups in their own settings. We are convinced that the need is there. We are further convinced that our methods are applicable to many different types of groups in many different settings. Finally, we are convinced that leadership for such groups can be found among those already working with the aged. That, indeed, is the next step—to encourage others to use the tools of mental health education in helping groups of older people to find themselves and each other, and through their own thinking and sharing to find new ways of fulfilling themselves, for living creatively, all the days of their lives.